D1632853

Block 1

Invention and innovation: an introduction

Ernie

This publication forms part of an Open University course T307 *Innovation: designing for a sustainable future*. Details of this and other Open University courses can be obtained from the Student Registration and Enquiry Service, The Open University, PO Box 197, Milton Keynes, MK7 6BJ, United Kingdom: tel. +44 (0)870 300 60 90, email general-enquiries@open.ac.uk

Alternatively, you may visit the Open University website at http://www.open.ac.uk where you can learn more about the wide range of courses and packs offered at all levels by The Open University.

To purchase a selection of Open University course materials visit http://www.ouw.co.uk, or contact Open University Worldwide, Walton Hall, Milton Keynes MK7 6AA, United Kingdom for a brochure. tel. +44 (0)1908 858793; fax +44 (0)1908 858787; email ouw-customer-services@open.ac.uk

The Open University
Walton Hall, Milton Keynes
MK7 6AA

First published 2006. Second edition 2010.

Edited, designed and typeset by the Open University.

Printed and bound in the United Kingdom by Martins the Printers Ltd.

ISBN 978 1 8487 3050 2

2.1

MIX
Paper from responsible sources
FSC® C013254

Contents

Introduction

In Section 1 I invite you to look around at the technological products in your home or at work and consider their development history and their impact on the lives of you and your family. I then define the key concepts associated with the process of invention, design, innovation and diffusion.

Section 2 considers what motivates individuals and organisations to invent in the first place and how individuals come up with ideas for new designs and inventions.

Section 3 examines how technical, financial and organisational obstacles have to be overcome in order to bring an invention to the market. Once on the market a number of factors influence how well an innovation will sell.

Section 4 considers if individual inventors still have a role to play in the innovation process as technology has become more complex and knowledge and skills more specialised.

Section 5 discusses the way in which innovations can have a disruptive impact on the way society organises itself and does business. I also deal with the idea of indefinite growth underpinned by innovation because this has been increasingly challenged as the environmental impacts became more visible.

Section 6 considers the factors that influence success in innovation. And I look at the possibility of forecasting technological development and steering innovation so that benefits outweigh the costs.

Aims and learning outcomes

Aims

Block 1 aims:

1   To provide an understanding of invention, design, innovation and diffusion as ongoing processes with a range of factors affecting success at each stage.

2   To provide an understanding of the factors that motivate individuals and organisations to invent, and the creative process by which individuals come up with ideas for new inventions and designs.

3   To provide an understanding of the obstacles that have to be overcome to bring an invention to market and the factors that influence the successful diffusion of an innovation into widespread use.

4   To enable you to discuss the extent to which individual inventors still have a role to play in the innovation process as technology has become more complex and knowledge and skills more specialised.

5   To help you appreciate the way in which innovations can have a disruptive impact on the way society organises itself and does business. And to make you aware that the idea of indefinite growth, underpinned by innovation, has been increasingly challenged as the environmental impacts became more visible.

6   To enable you to summarise the main factors that influence success in innovation. And to prompt you to discuss if it's possible to forecast future technological development. And to get you to ask if the benefits of innovation outweigh the costs.

Learning outcomes

After studying this block and carrying out the associated exercises, you should have achieved the following learning outcomes.

1   Knowledge and understanding

You should be able to:

1.1   Explain invention, design, innovation and diffusion as ongoing processes with a range of factors affecting success at each stage.

1.2   Explain how particular products you use have a history of invention and improvement, and appreciate the role that you and your family, as consumers, have played in this history.

1.3   Define key concepts such as invention, design, innovation, diffusion, product champion, entrepreneur, sustaining and disruptive innovation (see *Course Index and Glossary* for full list).

1.4   Explain the role of intellectual property in invention and innovation and list the various ways that inventors can protect their ideas.

1.5 Identify the range of reasons that motivate individuals and organisations to invent.

1.6 Explain the creative process by which individuals come up with ideas for new designs and inventions.

1.7 Explain the technology push, market pull, and coupling models of the innovation process and decide how well they offer a satisfactory explanation of the innovation process.

1.8 Identify and discuss the technical, financial and organisational obstacles that have to be overcome to bring an invention to the market.

1.9 Discuss the importance of choosing an appropriate design, materials and manufacturing process for a particular new product.

1.10 Explain the factors that influence how well an innovation will sell and how rapidly it is likely to diffuse into the market.

1.11 Give examples of disruptive innovations that can introduce a new way of operating in a particular industry, that can challenge existing companies and that can open up new markets for innovative products.

1.12 Discuss the extent to which individual inventors still have a role to play in the innovation process as technology has become more complex and knowledge and skills more specialised.

1.13 Explain the importance of teamwork and organised effort given the knowledge and resources needed for successful innovation.

1.14 List the main characteristics of inventive individuals and discuss the contributions they can still make to invention, design and innovation.

1.15 Identify and discuss the disruptive impact of developments in science-based innovations such as information and communication technologies and nanotechnology.

1.16 Discuss how a concern for the environment has become an important factor for designers, technologists and consumers of new products and processes; and discuss how this has led to the notion of sustainable innovation.

1.17 Summarise the main factors that influence success in innovation.

1.18 Discuss how well future technological development can be forecast.

2 Cognitive skills

You should be able to:

2.1 Analyse an innovation in terms of the various stages in its invention, design, innovation and diffusion.

2.2 Identify the reasons for the relative success or failure of a given innovation.

2.3 Analyse any innovation in terms of the evolutionary development of its design, materials, components and manufacturing processes.

2.4 Consider environmental impacts and sustainability when generating and selecting project ideas and solutions.

2.5 Analyse how well the future development of a given technology can be forecast.

3 Key skills

You should be able to:

3.1 Use the internet to obtain relevant information for block, project and assessment activities.

4 Practical and professional skills

You should be able to:

4.1 Apply associative thinking ideas to tackle problems requiring creativity.

1 Investigating the innovation process

1.1 Living with innovation

Picture an everyday scene. You're in a high street coffee shop. All around you people are drinking coffee. Some people are chatting with friends, others are using their mobile phone. A few individuals seem to be working – consulting their laptop computers, scribbling notes. In a corner of the coffee shop an internet café has been set up – like the one in Figure 1. At one table a couple of teenagers are laughing at a message in a chat room, while at another table an old chap searches the Web for something.

Figure 1　How predictable was mobile communications technology 100, 50 or 25 years ago? Who could have predicted an internet cafe?
Source: Mirrorpix

Now imagine this scene through the eyes of a technologist from 100 years ago. This is someone who has thought carefully about how technology and society might develop during the twentieth century. Putting aside his disappointment at not seeing any flying cars or people wearing silver spacesuits, some aspects of the scene will be familiar. People are still drinking coffee and talking as they did in 1906, although the range of coffees, the variety of accents and languages, and the mix of races and sexes might be surprising.

Surprising too may be the realisation that some of the people here are working in a leisure setting. The technologist had probably imagined that by now the working week would last only a few hours.

Most surprising perhaps will be the technological tools most people seem to be using. The technologist is aware of the telephone, which was invented about 30 years earlier. If he's sufficiently affluent he may have used one – about 7 per cent of households in London had a telephone by the early years of the twentieth century. But most of these twenty-first century people seem to have wireless pocket-size personal communicators they can use to send messages or speak to anyone anywhere in the world.

Some are using a handheld machine that contains thousands of pieces of information that can be accessed instantly, and can do calculations in a fraction of a second that would have taken a team of operators with mechanical calculators hours or even days. And these machines, like the only slightly larger versions in the corner, can be connected to a global brain from which the people can call up almost any information, news, idea, opinion or gossip that exists anywhere on the planet.

How much of this scene would have been predictable 100 years ago? And how many anticipated developments of technology, like flying cars, haven't come about? Well, don't be too hard on the technologist. Some of these technologies weren't even predicted as recently as 25 years ago. As many people have said before, hindsight is the only exact science.

Most of the changes in technology, compared to 100 years ago, are due to the continual inventive activity of a large number of people. At the most basic level many of us at some time or other have felt annoyed at the way some product works or doesn't work. Most of us don't do anything other than maybe form a vague idea about how a product or process might be improved. In some people, however, this inventive drive is so strong that they act on it.

What events and ideas spurred people to come up with thousands of inventions in the last 100 years?

Ron Hickman was a do-it-yourself enthusiast who damaged a chair being used to support a piece of wood he was sawing. Instead of merely being annoyed at the accident he set about designing and building a prototype of a combined workbench and sawhorse to prevent further damage to his furniture. This became the Workmate (Figure 2), which to date has sold well over 50 million units.

James Dyson was unhappy with the reduced suction power of his domestic vacuum cleaner as the bag filled with dust. So he took the industrial cyclone technology used to extract harmful particles by centrifugal force from factory paint shops and sawmills, scaled it down and applied it to improve the performance of domestic cleaners. His bagless cyclone cleaner has had worldwide success (Figure 3).

If you can't be sure people will want to buy a new product in large enough numbers, then it's a financial gamble to try to commercialise an invention. However there are big money rewards for any individual or company brave enough to take risks. The cumulative effect of this combined inventive and commercial drive has led to the sorts of changes observed by the visitor from 1906.

At the start of the twenty-first century technological innovation seems to be accelerating. This has resulted in an amazing variety of new products, processes and technical systems developed to meet ever more sophisticated sets of requirements. In the Westernised world at least innovation is widely believed to be vital for ensuring the economic prosperity not only of individuals and commercial organisations, but also of nations.

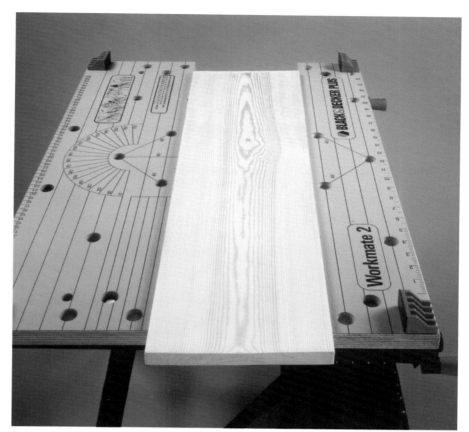

Figure 2 Black & Decker Workmate workbench, originally designed by Ron Hickman Source: DIY Picture Library

In 2003 the prime minister of the UK Tony Blair said,

> The creativity and inventiveness of our people is our country's greatest asset and has always underpinned the UK's economic success. But in an increasingly global world, our ability to invent, design and manufacture the goods and services that people want is more vital to our future prosperity than ever.
>
> Innovation, the exploitation of new ideas, is absolutely essential to safeguard and deliver high-quality jobs, successful businesses, better products and services for our consumers, and new, more environmentally friendly processes.

> (Department of Trade and Industry, 2003, p. 3)

Progress itself is often defined in terms of the ability of individuals and organisations to invent new products and processes, devise improvements to existing products, and make a success of selling such innovations on the market. Products developed over the last 100 years such as the telephone (originating in the 1870s), motor vehicles (1880s), television (1920s), and computers (1940s) have transformed the world and the way people organise their lives.

Figure 3 Dyson DC07 upright cyclone cleaner Source: courtesy of Dyson Ltd

Equally important, inventive skills have been applied to developing new materials and manufacturing processes, enabling new and improved products to be made more efficiently with lower labour and manufacturing costs and with less overall environmental impact. The invention of faster and more efficient processes has enabled the quality of innovative products to be steadily improved over the lifetime of a product – at the same time the price to customers has been reduced, therefore increasing availability and profits.

This process of steady improvement can continue for a long time, at least until the market is saturated or a newer innovation comes along that has a competitive advantage – cheaper, easier to use, more reliable or does the job better. Most mature, everyday products are now relatively cheaper than when they were introduced and certainly perform more reliably.

For example the ballpoint pen was invented by Laszlo Biro in 1938. The first Biro pen to go on sale in the UK in 1946 cost 55 shillings (£2.75), which was more than half the average weekly wage at the time (Figure 4). It required refills and service to be carried out by the retailer. However, in 1953, Marcel Bich developed a process for manufacture and assembly of ballpoint pens that dramatically increased the volume of production and reduced the cost of each pen. Nowadays you can buy a perfectly adequate, reliable ballpoint pen for a few pence. At the time of writing (2005) the BIC Cristal (Figure 5), direct descendant of the original Biro, cost less than 20 pence and more than 5 billion BIC ballpoints are being sold each year (around 14 million each day).

Figure 5   BIC Cristal ballpoint pen, 2005

The timescale for the widespread take-up (known as diffusion) of many innovations is shortening. For example it took radio 37 years to reach an audience of 50 million listeners, TV about 15 years to reach the same number of viewers and the World Wide Web just over 3 years to reach 50 million users.

Over the period since the invention of radio the UK and US populations increased by 1.5 and 3 times respectively, so population increase alone doesn't explain a tenfold increase in the take-up rate of innovative products. The industrial and social infrastructure has become increasingly effective at producing and selling new products. The increasing speed of diffusion of many innovations suggests we are experiencing revolutionary change.

However there is actually much continuity in the way in which innovation occurs and society adapts to it. Much has changed over the last 100 years but many of the institutions and much of the commercial

Figure 4   Announcement of the revolutionary new writing implement, the Biro, in 1946
Source: John Frost Historical Newspaper Service

structure of our society would be broadly recognisable to the visitor from the past. In reality change caused by innovation is more evolutionary and less transforming.

1.2   Exploring innovation

Before I look in more detail at what's involved in the processes of invention and innovation, I want you to consider your own experience of innovation as an end user.

Now attempt Exercise 1. Consider the impact of one innovation on you and your family and, using the internet, look briefly at the development history behind that innovation. You'll need to make notes summarising what you discover, so make sure you have some means of recording the information and your comments.

Exercise 1   Exploring innovation

Look around at technological products at home or at work. Pick a product that interests you.

1   Using an internet search engine such as Google (recommended), AlltheWeb, Ask Jeeves, or MetaCrawler (which searches other search engines) carry out a quick internet search for the history of your product's development.

A good start would be to find a timeline, which will show you the key stages in the development of the technology and the various individuals and companies likely to have been involved. Then you can investigate particular aspects of the timeline to reveal a more detailed picture.

If you spend around 1 hour on the search, you're likely to come up with a surprising amount of information. See how many of the following questions you can answer.

(a)   When and where was the product invented?

(b)   Who invented it?

(c)   What was innovative about it?

(d)   Was it invented in response to a need or because of developments in technology?

(e)   Was it an immediate success?

(f)   Has its design changed over time?

(g)   Has it led to any related or spin-off products?

2   Map your own or your family's experience of this product onto its development history by answering the following questions.

(a)   When did you or your family first get the product?

(b)   How long were you aware of the product before buying it?

(c)   Was it a new gadget or the latest version of a well-established product?

(d)   Did you delay buying it because of its price, the cost of using it or doubts about its reliability?

(e)   Have you since replaced it with an improved or updated version?

Discussion

Here's my own attempt at this exercise carried out for the telephone. If you've chosen the telephone, or you'd rather not see my results yet, then read no further until you've done the activity yourself.

Internet search results

I used Google to carry out a number of searches using various combinations of the words 'telephone', 'history', 'timeline', 'invention'. I followed up a range of sites, usually finding those associated with a university ('edu' for US sites, 'ac' in the UK) or a museum yielded the most authoritative information. Also the archives of companies associated with the telephone (BT in the UK; AT&T, Bell and Western Union in the US) contained some useful information. Finally many individual hobbyist sites contained some fascinating detail, although their accuracy needed to be treated with some scepticism and required double-checking with other sources.

When and where was the product invented? The accepted date is 1876 but a form of telephone may have been invented before then. It was first commercialised in the USA but a number of inventors in different countries had developed prototypes.

Who invented it? The accepted inventor is Alexander Graham Bell but claims have been made on behalf of other inventors.

What was innovative about it? The chief form of quick, distance communication at the time, the telegraph, was one-way, indirect and needed skilled operators to translate and transmit Morse code. The telephone offered instant, two-way speech communication directly between individuals and required no special skills to operate.

Was it invented in response to a need or because of developments in technology? It seems to have started with inventive individuals developing new technology. Then once this new means of communication became available increasing numbers of people wanted to use the telephone and a new need had been created.

Was it an immediate success? The telephone was by no means an immediate success but rather experienced a steady growth, starting with a small number of specialised users.

Has its design changed over time? Yes. Mouth and earpieces were amalgamated into a telephone set but still as separate items. As the technology improved, both transmitter and receiver were incorporated into a single handset and later a dial was added. Plastics permitted new shapes, and recently miniaturisation has allowed an increasing number of functions to fit into ever-smaller handsets.

Has it led to any related or spin-off products? The original telephone has evolved into a number of forms such as the mobile phone and the videophone. There have also been spin-off products based on the technology, such as sound reproduction devices.

A consumer's experience

When did you or your family first get the product? My parents first acquired a domestic telephone in 1968.

How long were you aware of the product before buying it? We'd been aware of the telephone all our lives but it seemed like a luxury item.

Was it a new gadget or the latest version of a well-established product? There didn't seem to be anything particularly novel about our first telephone.

On the surface the apparatus design had not changed significantly for 40 years, with a dial on the front and a large handset sitting on a cradle on top.

Did you delay buying it because of its price, the cost of using it or doubts about its reliability? At first a combination of cost and not knowing many people with a phone meant that there didn't seem to be any point in owning one. Reliability didn't seem to be a problem.

Have you since replaced it with an improved or updated version? Developments in the technology and increased competition following privatisation have resulted in a variety of cheap handsets and innovative features. That first handset my parents rented lasted us for 10 years but now my family replaces telephones frequently, reflecting the most recent innovation.

1.3 Inventing the telephone and living with the innovation

I will now elaborate on my answer from Exercise 1. I'm doing this because my internet search revealed more than I've written in the above answer, and to show that the invention of the telephone and its use by consumers is not as plain and simple as you may think. You were not expected to provide the kind of detail below and my search took much more than 1 hour.

1.3.1 When and where was the telephone invented?

I'd read in the past that the telephone was invented in 1876 by Alexander Graham Bell. However when I looked more closely at the history it turns out that the idea had been 'in the air' for almost half a century.

The distance communication technology of the time, the telegraph, was based on sending pulses of electricity along a wire to control an electromagnet at the receiving end. The sender completed an electric circuit by pressing a key and the receiver's electromagnet controlled a pen that made marks on a moving paper tape. Samuel Morse devised a code whereby the letters of the alphabet could be represented by different combinations of dots and dashes. Later, telegraph operators learned to interpret the Morse code from the sound made by the electromagnet and the paper tape became redundant.

In 1854 Charles Bourseul suggested that speaking close to a diaphragm would cause it to vibrate and that these vibrations could be used to make or break an electrical circuit, as in the telegraph. The process could then be reversed by a receiving diaphragm turning the signal back into speech. Bourseul didn't pursue this idea himself but it was taken up by other inventors. A self-taught German physicist and schoolteacher, Philipp Reis, demonstrated a form of telephone based on these ideas in 1861. Although it could transmit music and certain other sounds along a wire his 'telephon' could not transmit intelligible speech. Moreover Reis suffered from ill health and lack of resources so did not patent or develop his prototype.

In Italy, Innocenzo Manzetti had been working on an automaton since 1849. His attempts to make his robot speak led him to develop a prototype telephone that was demonstrated to the Italian press in 1865.

It is said that his humble nature and lack of finance meant he didn't try to commercialise his prototype.

In 1871 an Italian immigrant to the USA, Antonio Meucci, filed a caveat for his 'teletrofono' invention based on a communication link he had rigged up between his basement lab and his second-floor bedroom to keep in touch with his ailing wife. (A caveat is a warning to others that he was in the process of inventing a device and has a general description of the invention not yet perfected.) Once again though, like Reis, Meucci suffered from illness and lack of resources. Not only could he not afford to convert his caveat into a full patent application, he couldn't afford the annual renewal fee and allowed his caveat to expire. In 2001 in a resolution acknowledging Meucci's contribution to the invention of the telephone, the US Congress said, 'if Meucci had been able to pay the $10 fee to maintain the caveat after 1874, no patent could have been issued to Bell'.

Bell was an elocution teacher of deaf pupils who was working on a device to translate sound into visible patterns that would allow deaf people to 'see' speech. While working on this device he realised the potential for improving the telegraph if a wave of undulating current could be transmitted along the wires instead of the existing intermittent pulses. This would allow a larger number of signals to be transmitted on the same telegraph circuit – each signal using a different musical note. This would make the system more efficient and reduce the need to erect many more new lines to cope with the growth in traffic.

Bell was among a number of inventors racing to be the first to produce a working prototype of what became known as the musical or harmonic telegraph (Figure 6). On 3 June 1875, while working on a prototype of the harmonic telegraph, Bell heard the sound of his assistant Watson plucking a metal reed on the sending device. After further experimentation Bell filed an application for a patent – said to be the single most valuable patent in history – on 14 February 1876 for an 'improvement to telegraphy' in which the transmission of 'noises or sounds' was merely one of the 'other uses to which these instruments may be put'. There was no mention of speech. Amazingly, however, only a few hours later another inventor, Elisha Gray, filed a caveat at the US Patent Office for a similar device. In other words to say the telephone was invented in 1876 doesn't tell the whole story – invention is an ongoing process not a one-off event.

1.3.2 Who invented the telephone?

The popular image of Bell inventing the telephone, while it has some truth, is by no means the whole story. The two most significant players in the invention of a practical working telephone were Bell and Elisha Gray.

Gray was the co-owner and chief scientist of a company that manufactured telegraphic equipment. Bell's patent description had sound transmission as a minor purpose. But Gray's caveat declared that the main purpose of his device was 'to transmit the tones of the human voice through a telegraphic circuit and reproduce them at the receiving end of the line, so that actual conversations can be carried on

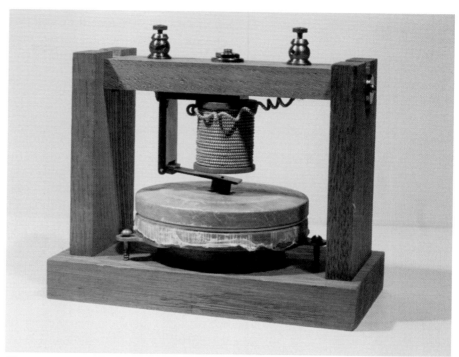

Figure 6 Bell's original telephone that first transmitted sound on 3 June 1875 – though Bell's first intelligible words of, 'Mr. Watson, come here, I want you', were not transmitted until 6 March 1876, a few weeks after the patent was applied for Source: Science Photo Library

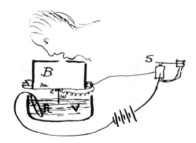

Figure 7(a) Drawing made by Bell of his design for an 'improvement to telegraphy' comprising a mouthpiece into which the user is talking and a speaker (centre right) to reproduce the sound Source: Science Photo Library

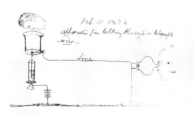

Figure 7(b) Drawing made by Elisha Gray of his design for an 'apparatus for talking through a telegraph wire'. Dated 'Feb 11 1876', 3 days before Bell and Gray's submissions were logged by the US Patent Office, the drawing clearly indicates a talker and a listener. Source: Science Photo Library

by persons at long distances apart'. Although Bell had built a prototype it wasn't a working telephone system, and while his early devices worked as receivers they never worked well as transmitters. In fact Gray's idea was sounder in concept than Bell's (including using liquid in the transmitter, an idea that Bell later adopted, some say copied), and Gray's intentions were clearer, but he hadn't built a working prototype either (Figure 7). The US patent system of the time didn't require inventors to produce a working prototype.

Gray chose to register his detailed specification as an incomplete invention, while Bell registered his partial specification as a complete invention. On the one hand it could be said that Bell was displaying the self-confidence needed by any inventor. However it was discovered in a Congressional inquiry 10 years later that an official from the Patent Office had informed Bell's lawyers of the *content* of Gray's caveat rather than just of its existence. Therefore when, a few weeks later, Bell was called to explain the similarities of his patent to one he had been granted a year earlier for a harmonic telegraph, it is suggested that he was able to use inside information to persuade the examiner that his was a new device – the telephone. A patent was granted to Bell in March 1876.

When doubts finally emerged about the propriety of Bell's original patent the US government brought a case in 1887 to annul the Bell patent on the grounds of 'fraud and misrepresentation'. However the claims could not be substantiated, most of the rival claimants had died or been bought off and the Bell patent was due to expire in 1893. To quote Congress, 'the case was discontinued as moot without ever reaching the underlying issue of the true inventor of the telephone entitled to the patent'.

To be fair Gray never claimed to be the sole inventor of the telephone but seemed to believe it was a case of 'simultaneous invention'. However with both men intent on exploiting the invention commercially it was inevitable that there would be a patent dispute. Gray lined up with Western Union, which funded his research, and which had obtained control of Thomas Edison's patent for a carbon transmitter. The giant telegraph company had set up a subsidiary, the American Speaking Telephone Company, to exploit the emerging technology that was being greeted enthusiastically by some of their best telegraph customers, the New York stockbrokers. Bell had a growing organisation on his side to exploit his invention – the Bell Telephone Company had become National Bell.

When Western Union started to use a system incorporating Edison's transmitter but Bell's receiver, National Bell resorted to the courts to stop it. At the same time Bell had Emile Berliner (later the inventor of the gramophone) working to produce a rival transmitter to go with Bell's superior receiver – and to bypass Edison's patent.

In 1879 an agreement was finally reached that saw Western Union agree to drop its counter-suits and sign over its own telephone patents. Apparently Western Union thought the telephone would only ever be a rival to the telegraph over short distances. In exchange National Bell agreed to drop its cases, buy out its rival's subscribers and equipment and pay Western Union a 20 per cent commission on each telephone rental for the remaining 15 years of the patents (this eventually totalled $7m). In addition Gray was paid $100 000 and Western Electric (Gray's company) was contracted as Bell's sole equipment supplier – an arrangement that lasted for almost 100 years.

Although there were many more patent cases brought both by and against Bell, Gray's had been the most significant. From this point on it was Bell's name and company that were associated with the invention and development of the telephone.

So the identification of a particular individual as the inventor of a new technology is not necessarily straightforward. Boldness and determination, allied with sufficient resources and a good support team – especially good patent lawyers – seem to be just as important as technical ingenuity. There also seems to be an element of history being written by the winners.

1.3.3 What was innovative about the telephone?

The most obvious innovative aspect was that speech was being transmitted, so in principle anyone could use a telephone for communication. The use of the telegraph required skilled operatives. A message had to be translated into the dots and dashes of Morse code and transmitted using a single keypad making and breaking the connection in an electrical circuit. At the other end of the wire another Morse operator translated the received clicks into the words of the message. With the telephone no specialised skills or training were needed to use it and the efficiency of communication was not limited by the speed and translating ability of the Morse operators. As a means of communicating across distance the telephone was easier to use and more efficient. Quite a competitive advantage.

However for early versions of the telephone much of this advantage was merely potential. It needed improvements in performance and a considerable growth in the telephone network before significant numbers of people were prepared to switch from the telegraph. Subsequent innovations, such as the manual exchange, pay phones, the automatic exchange, metering, trunk dialling and the more recent introduction of digital systems, have all contributed to the spread of the telephone as a technological product.

1.3.4 Was the telephone invented in response to a need or because of developments in technology?

As with many truly innovative technologies it's difficult to claim that people were demanding its invention. Most people were satisfied with the existing means of communicating across distances. It took a great deal of imagination to foresee that the ability to speak to others at a distance would eventually replace the telegraph in business and the letter in personal communications. People weren't expressing a need to be able to communicate more rapidly but once the means became available to do so they steadily took advantage of the new technology. Then positive feedback took over and the better the technology became the more people got used to its benefits and the greater their need became for more innovation.

Developments in technology can create a need that provides a ready market for improved versions of the technology. And so it goes on.

1.3.5 Was the telephone an immediate success?

By the end of 1876 Bell had managed to build an experimental device that could carry a conversation across 2 miles of wire. The following year the first operational telephone line was erected over the 5 miles between Charles Williams' factory in Boston and his home in Somerville. It was done there because Bell had conducted some of his experimental work in Williams' electrical workshops a couple of years earlier. These first telephones were still fairly crude devices and arranged in pairs to connect two particular sites – there was no network. The sound they produced was weak and indistinct, and deteriorated with distance.

There was immediate scepticism expressed about the telephone from the telegraph companies and others. It wasn't so much that the telegraph companies saw the telephone as a threat, at least not in the early days. It was more that they had their own well-established technology, employed most of the people with any expertise in this area and saw no need to change.

Furthermore not everyone can appreciate the potential of a very new technology. Even Bell might not have realised the significance of the invention to start with. Later in the same year, after he was granted his patent, he and his financial backer offered to sell the patent to the Telegraph Company, which was the forerunner of Western Union. The offer was turned down, allegedly with the new invention being dismissed as 'hardly more than a toy'.

New technologies can encounter resistance from people with a stake in established technologies. For a new technology to succeed it must be clear what advantage it has to offer over existing technology, and it has to capture enough users to make itself economically viable. For a decade or more after its invention there was still some uncertainty about the best use for the telephone. A London company offered multiple headsets for connecting telephone subscribers and their friends and family to theatres, concerts and church services. In Paris and Budapest an all-day telephone news service was offered – this actually continued for 30 or 40 years. But any potential for high-quality sound from the telephone had been sacrificed in the interest of maximising the number of conversations that could be carried along a single wire. In other words it was designed for one-to-one conversation and that became its main function.

The first significant users of the telegraph had been the stock market and newspapers who contributed to its widespread diffusion. These two groups were also among the early users of the telephone and Bell's marketing was almost exclusively aimed at commercial users. Even in the USA the telephone was mostly a business tool for the first 50 years of its development. It wasn't until after the Second World War that a majority of US households had a private telephone.

So the telephone was by no means an immediate success but rather experienced a steady growth, starting with a small number of specialised users and gradually diffusing into more general and widespread use.

1.3.6 Has telephone design changed over time?

As you can see from Figure 8 the design of the telephone has changed considerably over its lifetime, reflecting the improvements in technology, materials, components and manufacturing processes. Figures 8(a) to (f) show some of the early progress. Figure 8(a) is a replica of Bell's 'liquid transmitter' of 1876 and 8(b) is a Bell telephone and terminal panel from 1877 showing the adaptation for two-way conversation. Edison's wall telephone (Figure 8c) was developed by 1880 and the classic 'candlestick' table top phone (Figure 8d) by 1900. As the technology improved both transmitter and receiver were incorporated into a single handset (Figure 8e), and once automatic exchanges had been invented room had to be found for a dial (8f, the Strowger automatic dial telephone, 1905). The appearance of synthetic plastics, starting with Bakelite in the 1920s, permitted new shapes (8g, Bakelite handset), and later developments led to colour being used in telephones for the first time (8h, plastic handset from the 1960s; 8i, Trimphone, 1970s). Dials were gradually superseded by push buttons (8j, Keyphone, 1972). Finally digitalisation and miniaturisation have challenged designers to fit an increasing number of functions into ever-smaller handsets. Figure 8(k) shows Motorola's MicroTAC personal cellular phone, which was the smallest and lightest on the market in 1989, and Figure 8(l) is Samsung's A800 'hinged' mobile phone of 2004.

(a)

(b)

(c)

(d)

(e)

(f)

(g)

(h)

(i)

(j)

(k)

(l)

Figure 8   Since its invention the design of the telephone has evolved Sources: (a) to (g) Science & Society Picture Library; (h) Science Photo Library; (i) Sam Hallas; (k) Northwood Images

1.3.7 Has the telephone led to any related or spin-off products?

There have been a number of branches of the telegraph and the telephone family tree where research and experiment into one technology have contributed to the development of another.

An early example was Edison inventing the phonograph. He'd been working on a telegraph repeater to record telegraph signals using a stylus to vibrate onto and indent a sheet of paper. The idea was that when the indented paper passed across the stylus again the indentations would cause identical vibrations and the telegraph message would be repeated exactly. Edison was also experimenting to improve the telephone.

When feeling the vibrations caused when sound passed through the diaphragm in a telephone mouthpiece, Edison realised that the repeater idea could be applied to the human voice being transmitted by the telephone. His first working prototype of the phonograph was hand-cranked and used tinfoil as the recording medium (Figure 9). Though there was something almost miraculous about hearing the human voice reproduced by this simple mechanical device there was no obvious use for it, particularly when the quality of recording was so poor. One of Edison's first ideas was to use it to record telephone conversations for posterity. After the initial excitement Edison abandoned the phonograph to work on the electric light.

Figure 9 **Edison's earliest model of the phonograph (1877) consisted of three main parts: a diaphragm and needle for capturing and transforming the sound; a hand-cranked cylinder covered with tinfoil on which the sound was recorded; another needle and diaphragm for replaying the sound**
Source: Science & Society Picture Library

Ten years later, under pressure from Bell who was developing an improved version of the phonograph, Edison finally produced a commercial phonograph using an electric motor and hard wax-coated cylinders that delivered much better sound quality. Around the same time Emile Berliner was inventing a means of recording onto a flat wax-coated zinc disk. Even this was initially regarded and marketed as a toy but eventually the gramophone formed the basis of a huge industry for selling recorded music.

Another of the branches led to radio and then mobile telephony. The work of Bell, Edison and others on improving the telegraph and transmitting sound along wires led eventually to wireless transmission – Marconi was transmitting Morse code messages from ship to shore in 1897 and eventually across the Atlantic in 1901. The first commercial transatlantic radio voice service began in 1927. The first radio-telephone service for vehicles was introduced in the US in 1946.

In 1947 microwave radio transmissions started to be used for long-distance telephony and by the early 1960s telecommunications satellites were being used for round-the-world contact. The first portable cellular phone appeared in 1979. Today's mobile phones might seem like a different product from Bell's early prototypes but there's a continuous line of scientific discoveries and developments in technology and materials connecting the two (Figure 10).

1.3.8 A consumer's experience of innovation

First phone in 1968

As I mentioned earlier my parents first acquired a domestic telephone in 1968 – more than 90 years after its invention.

Before then other ways of communicating seemed good enough. In the early 1950s in our street of around 100 houses only one family had a private telephone. My family used public call boxes occasionally but we didn't know many people with their own phone so not many calls needed to be made. When we needed to communicate with people at a distance we sent a letter. In emergencies or for urgent communications we sent or received telegrams – but these were usually reserved for bad news.

Product awareness

My parents and I had been aware of the telephone all our lives but it seemed like a luxury item and was lower in our priorities than, say, a car (that we bought in 1956) or a television (1958). Even by 1970 only around 30 per cent of households in the UK had a home telephone – this had risen to 95 per cent by the year 2000.

New but familiar

There didn't seem to be anything particularly novel about our first telephone. On the surface the design had not changed significantly for 40 years, consisting of a dial on the front and a large handset sitting on a cradle on top. The most obvious changes were in the materials used – moulded plastic had replaced Bakelite and metal. These material changes in our 1968 telephone had been introduced in 1959 with the launch of the 700-series telephone (Figure 11). This was much lighter than previous designs with lightweight components and a plastic body.

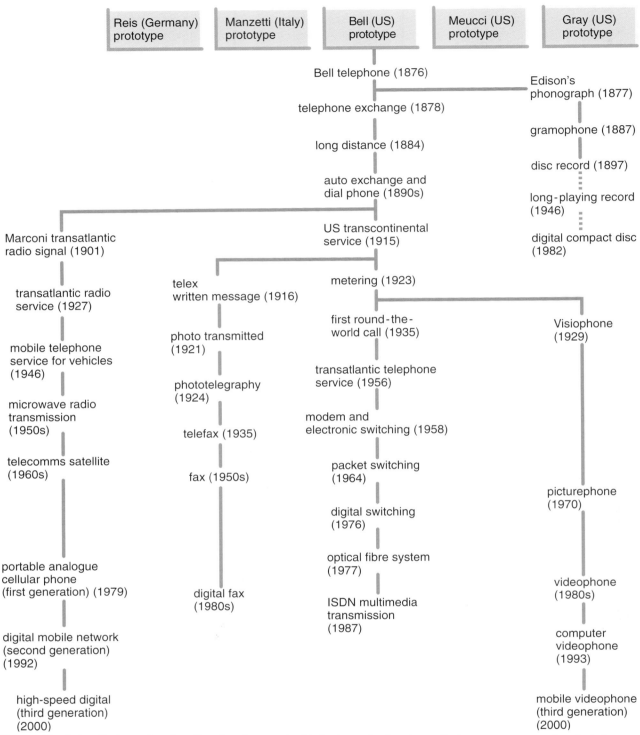

Figure 10 A family tree showing the development of telephone technology. It shows a progression but does not try to show every kind of product developed.

Also, for the first time, telephones were available in a range of six colours (ours was green), marking the demise of black as the standard telephone colour. The now familiar curled cord connecting the handset to the body also made its first appearance with this design change.

In those days the apparatus and the line were both rented from the Post Office but for the first time it was possible to exercise some consumer choice. The first choice was over the colour. Even as late as

Figure 11 700-series plastic-bodied telephone, launched in 1959 Source: courtesy of Telephones UK

1968, limitations in the capacity of telephone exchanges meant the norm was to have a party line shared with at least one other household. The other choice available was to have a dedicated line, although that was more expensive to have installed. We were relatively unusual in having our own dedicated line.

Product price, reliability and reasons for buying

We acquired a telephone when we did for a mixture of reasons. When my mother got a job our family had more disposable income to spend on consumer goods. Costs of owning a phone had fallen in relative terms as use of the telephone spread, bringing its running costs within our price range. More of our family and friends were getting telephones so it began to make more sense for us to get one so we could keep in touch. Reliability didn't seem to be a problem. Another significant factor was that my mother worked for social services and her employer wanted to be able to contact her quickly as part of her job. So the requirement for instant communication was spreading into the culture of certain types of occupation.

Once ownership of phones reached a certain proportion of the population its take-up seemed to gather momentum. And once people began to experience the ease and convenience offered by having a telephone in their own home it became part of their expectations of modern living. For increasing numbers of people, owning a phone became a necessity rather than a luxury.

Telephones since 1968

The ending of the Post Office monopoly in 1981 and the introduction of competition, firstly to the apparatus supply market and then to the provision of phone services, led to an increase in competing products and a spread of the technology. That first handset my parents rented lasted us for 10 years.

Since competition was introduced and cheap handsets became available to buy, most of us seem to replace our handsets much more frequently. This has been stimulated by an increasing variety of innovative features offered over the years – push-buttons, built-in answer phones, handsets combined with a radio, novelty handsets, cordless phones with several handsets, and so on. In contrast to my parents' house of the 1960s, my own family has two telephone lines, two computers connected to the internet, and we have three handsets in various parts of the house. In addition every member of the family has their own mobile phone, a product of a merger between the telephone and radio timelines. But that's another story.

1.3.9 What has been learnt from the history of the telephone?

Here are some points about invention and innovation that seem to have emerged from considering the case of the telephone.

- Invention is an ongoing process not a one-off event.

- It's not always possible to identify one individual as the inventor of a new technological product – even in well-known cases.

- Boldness and determination, allied with sufficient resources and a good support team – especially good patent lawyers – seem to be just as important as technical ingenuity.

- It can take a great deal of imagination to foresee how a new technology might be used, particularly for potential financial backers not directly involved with the development of the technology.

- An innovation needs a competitive advantage over existing technologies or products in order to succeed.

- The success of an innovation depends on regular improvements to its performance, reliability and design. This is usually achieved by building on a series of innovations in supporting technology, improvements in manufacturing processes, component performance, new materials use and so on.

- The affordability of innovative products is important – this is related to the cost of its manufacture and the relative affluence of buyers.

- There's a relationship between new technology and needs – new technologies can create new markets that provide an incentive to make further improvements to the technology.

- A group of early, sometimes specialised users of an innovation can play an important part in giving momentum to its sales.

- As the use of an innovation spreads it changes from being a novelty or luxury to a necessity for increasing numbers of people.

- There are fashions in innovative products, shaped by marketing and advertising, which can stimulate demand for a particular product.

- Governments can affect the context for innovation in particular areas of technology.

- There are factors that can suppress or delay the spread of an innovation, particularly in the early years of its development: patent disputes over ownership; resistance from people with a stake in established technologies; protective inertia in business and institutional structures resisting radical change.

- Research and experimentation into one technology can contribute to the development of another spin-off technology.

1.4   Key course concepts

Before I go any further I will establish the meaning of some of the key concepts from the course that you will encounter throughout this block.

The key concepts from *Innovation: designing for a sustainable future* elaborated in this block are:

- inventor

- invention

- design

- product champion

- entrepreneur

- improver

- innovation

- dominant design

- robust design

- lean design

- radical innovation

- incremental innovation

- sustaining innovation

- disruptive innovation

- process innovation

- diffusion and suppression

- intellectual property and patents.

Although innovation is the term applied to one particular stage, it is also common to talk about the whole process from invention to diffusion as the innovation process. (These and other definitions can also be found in the *Course Index and Glossary*.)

To illustrate these concepts I will use the example of a significant invention with which you are familiar and that has come to symbolise the inspired moment at the heart of invention – the electric light. This example also illustrates the range of factors behind the success of one of the most famous inventors of all time, Thomas Edison. The irony, as you will discover, is that there was no clear 'Eureka!' moment in this invention. It was the product of sheer hard work and demonstrated Edison's famous saying in a newspaper interview, 'Genius is 1 per cent inspiration and 99 per cent perspiration'.

The DVD contains video material illustrating Edison's work at every stage of the innovation process from generating ideas, assembling a team to build and test prototypes, raising finance, and manufacturing and marketing his new products. The material considers the extent to which Edison established many of the contours of the modern world by organising the large-scale development of new technological products.

1.4.1 Inventors and inventions

inventor
individual or group able to generate an idea for a new or improved device, product or process

An inventor is an individual or group able to generate an idea for a new or improved device, product or process. The idea must then be transformed into concrete information in the form of a description, sketch or model.

invention
idea, concept or design for a new or improved device, product or process available as a description, sketch or model

An invention is an idea, concept or design for a new or improved device, product or process that is available as concrete information in the form of a description, sketch or model.

So an inventor may have many ideas for new products or improvements to existing processes, say, but these do not constitute an invention until the ideas have been transformed into something real, such as drawings or a prototype with the potential for practical application. As you will see later on, the conditions for granting a patent to protect an invention from being copied are that the invention must be new, must not be obvious to someone who knows about the subject and must be capable of industrial application.

Given that the process of invention takes place over time it is often not possible to be precise about the exact moment that an inventive idea becomes an invention. For example in 1878 the prolific US inventor, Thomas Edison, began work on inventing an incandescent lamp powered by electricity. He was enthused by a new kind of generator that had been developed to power a small arc-light system and realised the commercial possibilities of being the first to provide a large-scale electric lighting system. He had a vision of lighting up an entire city district with such a generator.

However the arc-light (bright light produced by a continuous electric arc leaping between two electrodes) suffered from two problems: burn-out of the tips of its electrodes meant regular replacement, and the problem of controlling the gap between the electrodes when they were constantly being burned up by the arc. Edison saw the need for inventing an electric lamp that would be effective and long lasting. He thought that the solution might lie in the incandescent lamp – that is, a lamp in which light is produced by using electricity to heat some substance to a high temperature, causing it to glow.

Others had been trying for years to achieve this goal, in fact the first patent on an incandescent lamp was taken out in Britain in 1841. The situation of many people working towards solving the same technological problem is common and often results in simultaneous invention – as you saw with the invention of the telephone. The most notable of these other inventors was Joseph Swan, an Englishman who had produced a design that featured a carbonised paper filament that glowed inside a glass when electricity was passed through it (Figure 12). The air was evacuated from the inside of the bulb so that oxygen would not cause the filament to burn up. However no one, including Swan, had managed to produce a filament that would glow for a useful length of time before being destroyed.

Figure 12   On the left is Swan's experimental carbon pencil lamp, 1878–9. On the right is the first prototype of Edison's incandescent lamp, 1879.
Source: Science & Society Picture Library

Edison's challenge was to find a suitable material for the filament that would permit a bright glow without burning up too quickly. He had ideas about how it might be done but it took a year of searching for and experimenting with thousands of different filament materials. He also searched for a method of achieving the necessary vacuum inside the light bulb. Eventually he produced a working prototype of his carbon filament lamp in October 1879. This consisted of a thread of carbonised cotton bent into the shape of a horseshoe and mounted inside a glass bulb (Figure 12, right) that had the air sucked out of it (Figure 13). When connected to an electric current the new 'electric candle' burned for almost 2 days.

Figure 13   Light bulb evacuation pumps

This apparatus was a combination of several existing technologies – Geissler and Sprengel's mercury pumps and McLeod's vacuum gauge. After only a few weeks of improvements in late 1879, Edison's team could evacuate a bulb to a millionth of an atmosphere in 20 minutes.

This first reliable working prototype could be said to be the invention. However before the electric light could be offered for sale to customers there was still a great deal of work to be done by Edison and his team of workers at his Menlo Park laboratory in north-east USA (Figure 14).

Figure 14   Edison's Menlo Park laboratory with experimental light bulb apparatus on the left, in front of a table of batteries

Questions in the text

This block has questions in some sections to get you to think about points raised in the text. The questions below are the first example of this. Sometimes there will just be a question, sometimes I will give a short answer.

Can you think of an inventor other than those named in this block?

I thought of Owen MacLaren, the retired engineer and grandfather who invented the lightweight, foldable baby buggy in the 1960s.

Can you think of a recent invention other than those in this block?

The proximity card is fairly new. It gives access to secure buildings when it is held near to an electronic sensor that is connected to an electric door lock.

1.4.2 Designs

design

drawings, instructions or models that contain the information for the manufacture of a product or the introduction of a process

A design comprises drawings, instructions or models that contain all the information for the manufacture of a product or the introduction of a process or system.

So Edison's early prototypes were different designs that *physically embodied* the new ideas on which his invention was based. But developing an invention in a laboratory or workshop is one thing, manufacturing an innovation to sell to others is a different matter.

Edison quickly realised that he needed to develop a complete electric lighting system, not just the electric lamp. Further, Edison had to ensure that his electric light and its related subsystems could be reproduced on the large scale that would be required to achieve commercial success. This involved producing designs of every component of his electric lighting system, in other words specific plans, drawings and instructions to enable the manufacture of products, processes or systems related to his invention (Figure 15). So design has a vital role to play in the commercial manufacture of new inventions, to specify and communicate what is to be made.

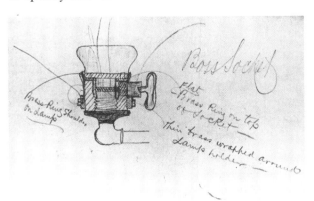

Figure 15   Design for screw socket, September 1880 Source: Edison National Historic Site

Edison's long-time associates, Edward H. Johnson and John Ott, were principally responsible for designing fixtures in the autumn of 1880. Their work resulted in the screw socket and base very much like those widely used today.

Edison and his team continued to develop and improve the lamp itself and the related devices necessary for reliable, large-scale lighting systems. They worked on techniques for creating better vacuums inside glass bulbs, improvements to the design of generators and distribution systems, and so on.

1.4.3 Product champion

Throughout the development of this innovation Edison endeavoured, by means of persuasive argument and demonstrations of progress, to convince those people who were in a position to help further the success of the electric light that it had great potential. These people included financiers who could provide capital for more research and development, industrialists who might install it in their factories, and politicians who might agree to the large-scale city installation of a lighting system.

product champion

individual or group committed to promoting the development of a new or improved product, process or system

This is a key role in the development of any invention; it needs a product champion. This will be an individual or group committed to promoting the development of a certain product, process or system.

Usually such championing takes place in an institutional context where the champion is trying to persuade the organisation that it is worth investing in a particular new product, or is prepared to defend an innovative product from attack once the process of development is under way. Sometimes, however, this takes place outside an organisation, where a sympathetic supporter will promote the qualities of an invention to those who might be willing to finance its development. If no outside support is forthcoming, or if even more support is needed to give momentum to the innovation process, the original inventor will need to take on the additional role of champion, as did Edison.

1.4.4 Entrepreneur

From this it is clear that money is a key requirement for transforming an invention into an innovation. Money pays for the people and equipment needed to refine the invention into a practical working prototype, and money pays for manufacturing it.

entrepreneur

persuasive individual or group providing the resources or organisation necessary to turn an invention into an innovation

A key role in providing this vital monetary support is played by the entrepreneur. This is a persuasive individual or group providing the resources and organisation necessary to turn the invention into an innovation.

Entrepreneurs are likely to be involved at an early stage of an innovation's development, either taking the risk of investing their own money or raising money for a project from others. Most people with money to invest will be inclined to wait until it is clearer whether an innovation is going to be successful before investing. Part of the task of the entrepreneur is to persuade them to take a risk. It is often the case that at the early stage of the innovation process an individual inventor or entrepreneur is unable to persuade people to risk investing in a new and untried invention. In the absence of the necessary financial support an inventor can either give up or take on the entrepreneurial role themselves. Section 4 includes examples of the activities of inventor-entrepreneurs.

Edison was one such inventor-entrepreneur. He used earnings from the commercial success of his earlier inventions – mainly related to improvements to the telegraph – together with some outside investment to build his Menlo Park workshops in 1876 (Figure 16). Edison and his team of technicians and mechanics at Menlo Park produced 400 patented inventions over the next 6 years including the microphone, the phonograph and the vacuum tube, which was later used in wireless telegraphy. This innovative laboratory therefore provided Edison with a firm technical base from which to develop the electric light, and freedom from the monetary pressures that bring down many inventors if they are unable to secure a quick return on investment in their invention. However Edison was not typical of inventor-entrepreneurs. His reputation for commercially successful inventions was so high that within a few weeks of announcing his intention to develop electric lighting, financiers were queuing up to invest in the Edison Electric Light Company – a situation the majority of inventors can only dream about.

Even Edison though could not combine perfectly the creative skills of invention and innovation with the business and managerial skills of the entrepreneur. It is said, 'he so totally mismanaged the businesses he started that he had to be removed from every one of them to save it' (Drucker, 1985).

Figure 16   Menlo Park laboratory staff, 1880. Edison is seated third from the left, second row from the top, holding a straw hat. Source: Edison National Historic Site

1.4.5 Improver

improver

individual or group whose concern is to do things better by making improvements to existing products or processes

At different stages of the process of invention, design and innovation there's a role that can be played by improvers. The improver is an individual or group whose concern is to do things better by making improvements to existing products or processes.

Such people can help transform an inventor's first prototype and early design into a commercial product. Edison's team at Menlo Park included a number of engineers, chemists and mathematicians who contributed to the improvement of the electric light, as well as other inventions.

Another contribution of improvers is at a slightly later stage in the innovation process when they can make incremental improvements to other people's inventions. For example in 1877 Edison developed a carbon transmitter that helped improve Bell's recently invented telephone.

1.4.6 Innovation

innovation

new or improved product, process or system that has reached the point of first commercial introduction – invention becomes innovation

The point at which the electric light first became available on the market was the moment the invention became an innovation. So an innovation is a new or improved product, process or system that has reached the point of first commercial introduction.

Even this moment of achieving innovation is sometimes difficult to pinpoint in a particular case. The first full-scale use of the electric lamp outside of the laboratory was in May 1880 when Edison installed 115 of them on the new steamship *Columbia* at the suggestion of its owner, Henry Villard, who had become an enthusiast for the electric light after seeing a demonstration at Menlo Park (Figure 17). The electric system was more suitable than open-flame lighting in the confined spaces of a ship. It was so effective that it was 15 years before it was replaced with more modern equipment. However it could be argued that this was not the moment of innovation as there was an element of personal favour rather than it being a purely commercial transaction.

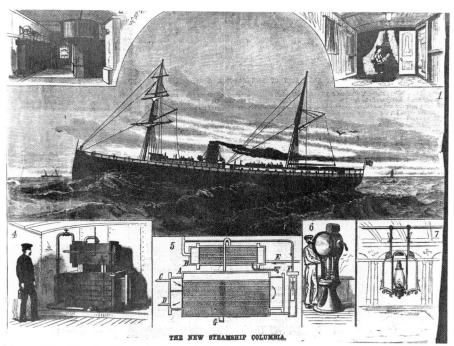

THE NEW STEAMSHIP COLUMBIA.

Figure 17   The first installation of the Edison system outside of Menlo Park was aboard the steamship, *Columbia* in 1880, shown here in a *Scientific American* engraving Source: Smithsonian Institute

It gave Edison an opportunity to put his light into operation under carefully managed conditions, as well as offering the chance for a public demonstration

One of the first commercial installations of Edison's complete electric light system (generators, distributing circuits and the bulbs) was for the lithography factory of Hinds, Ketcham & Company, New York, in early 1881. Electric lighting allowed the factory to operate at night without difficulty in distinguishing colours.

The first full-scale public demonstration of Edison's urban lighting system was along the Holborn Viaduct in London (Figures 18 and 19). The first generator started up in January 1882 and the Holborn installation was a testing ground for a number of key elements of his more famous installation at Pearl Street Station in New York, which began service later that year.

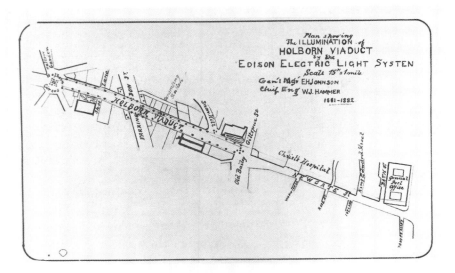

Figure 18   Plan for lighting the Holborn Viaduct, London Source: Smithsonian Institute

The Holborn Viaduct project was intended as a temporary demonstration, not a permanent commercial station. By choosing the viaduct, Edison's London agents were able to install the system quickly and with minimal cost because the electrical conduits could be hung underneath without excavations or the need for permits. The viaduct was a testing ground for several key elements of Edison's system, especially safety devices and regulating mechanisms.

1.4.6 Dominant design

In most examples of evolving technological innovation there is a period when rival designs are competing to outperform each other, both in what they do and how well they appeal to the consumer. Certain features of a product or process come to be recognised as meeting key needs and they are incorporated in subsequent improved versions of the design. Other features might meet too narrow a set of needs to be economical and are dropped.

dominant design
product whose form and function have evolved to become the accepted market standard

Gradually what emerges is a dominant design, which is the product whose form and function have evolved to become the accepted market standard.

The dominant design defines the expected appearance of a particular innovation and how it is meant to work. A dominant design is not necessarily the one with the best performance but its performance will be good enough so that, together with its other desirable features, it will meet the needs of many different types of user (Figure 20).

Figure 19 Edison's Jumbo dynamo. Site unknown but probably the Holborn Viaduct station, London, 1882.
Source: Edison National Historic Site

Figure 20 The Ediswan carbon-filament lamp, 1884 became a dominant design Source: Science & Society Picture Library

Edison and Swan had merged their electric light companies in 1883 rather than challenge each other's patents

Can you think of a dominant design other than those named in this block?

Examples I thought of were the office stapler, the briefcase and the wheelbarrow. Different manufacturers' versions of these products have common design features and similar overall appearance.

1.4.7 Robust design and lean design

In the case of the incandescent lamp the first dominant design had emerged by 1884, only 4 years after the first lamps had gone on public display around Menlo Park. It consisted of a screw-in metal base, a carbonised bamboo filament with platinum electrical wiring attached to a glass stem, all of which was sealed into a pear-shaped glass bulb that had been evacuated. This design was so successful that competitors did not try to devise a different design but merely copied Edison's; the company spent the next 7 years repeatedly suing rivals for infringement of the patents until its dominance was clearly established.

robust design

adaptable product that is more likely to be commercially successful because it is suitable for different uses

lean design

product that is highly optimised and likely to be less successful because it is only suitable for specific uses

radical innovation

product, process or system resulting from a technological breakthrough, or an application of a technology having a far-reaching impact

Further, a new product is more likely to be commercially successful if it is a robust design and suitable for different uses. A new product is likely to be less successful it if is a lean design, too highly optimised and only suitable for specific uses. So Edison's lamp was a robust design because it could fit into existing gas lamp brackets, and this increased its chances of catching on because it could make use of some of the existing infrastructure in homes and offices.

1.4.8 Radical innovation and incremental innovation

The electric light might be said to be an example of a radical innovation – a new product, process or system resulting from a technological breakthrough, or an application of a technology having a far-reaching impact.

Radical innovations can have a widespread and sometimes revolutionary impact on our lives and are said by some to account for technological progress. However, as you saw with the example of the telephone, most radical innovations are actually an accumulation of much smaller improvements, often carried out by many different individuals and organisations over time. The notion of the electric light might seem like a radical idea but it was actually the product of an attempt to provide a form of lighting that improved on existing methods. Apart from candles and oil lamps, these were mainly the gas light (increasingly used in urban homes but with an associated fire hazard and impact on air quality) and existing electric arc-lighting (too dazzling for domestic use and suffering from control and maintenance problems).

Furthermore the provision of an effective system of electric lighting depended upon the steady incremental improvement in a range of associated technologies – glass blowing, vacuum pumping, electricity distribution, and so on.

Therefore the application of the label radical innovation depends on the context and the time scale. Radical innovations are often incremental in terms of their scientific and technological development but radical in their application and ultimate impact on society. Also the early, often unreliable, examples of an innovation might not seem to be a significant improvement on existing technology until improvements in performance encourage more people to buy the innovation, which increases its impact.

Can you think of another example of a radical innovation?

I think the passenger aeroplane and man-made fibres used in clothing were radical innovations when they first appeared. They have had an impact on people's lives, for example the aeroplane brought tourism to remote communities.

So an apparently radical innovation actually involves much incremental innovation – technical modifications to an existing product, process or system and sometimes known as evolutionary innovation. The analogy with biological evolution is not precise however because technological evolution involves conscious and deliberate choice.

incremental innovation
technical modifications to an existing product, process or system and sometimes known as evolutionary innovation

Can you think of an incremental innovation?

There are kitchen utensils sold under the brand name of Good Grips. They are designed to be easy for disabled people to use. I also thought online ticket booking could be considered to be an incremental innovation, although it also has some features of a disruptive innovation.

1.4.9 Sustaining innovation and disruptive innovation

As it's sometimes difficult to say whether a particular innovation is radical or incremental, a useful distinction made recently is between sustaining innovations and those that are disruptive. You'll read more about these ideas in Section 3.

sustaining innovation
new or improved product that meets the needs of most current customers and serves to sustain leading firms

Briefly a sustaining innovation is a new or improved product that meets the needs of most current customers and serves to sustain leading firms in their market position. So in this context improvements to gas lighting, say, would be sustaining innovations.

disruptive innovation
product or technology that challenges existing companies to ignore or embrace technical change – new companies often emerge to exploit it

By contrast, a disruptive innovation is a new or improved product or technology that challenges existing companies to ignore or embrace technical change.

Often new companies emerge to exploit a disruptive innovation. Such innovations can seem unpromising in the early stages of their development. However if they go on to become successful they can form new markets in which established companies lose their market leadership. Edison's electric light led to the creation of a whole new system for the generation and supply of electricity and its conversion into lighting. This in turn required a whole infrastructure of companies to supply raw materials and components for what became a new industry. It had a disruptive effect on the existing market for lighting.

1.4.10 Process innovation

process innovation
improvement in the organisation and/or method of manufacture that often leads to reduced supply costs or benefits to customers

Once a product innovation is well established creative energies tend to turn towards incremental improvements and process innovation, which is an improvement in the organisation and/or method of manufacture that often leads to reduced supply costs.

These two factors typically result in a better-performing product yet one that can be manufactured in less time, possibly using fewer components and possibly using machinery operated by less skilled, less costly workers. For example incremental improvements in the type of filaments used, tungsten gradually replacing carbon, led to a threefold increase in the efficiency of the electric light. And process innovations made the manufacturing more efficient – for example hand blowing of bulbs was replaced by a semi-automated machine in 1894.

All of these process innovations can lead to a dramatic fall in the production costs, and therefore the sales price, of an innovation in the early years of its use. For example, after 15 years of production, the number of steps involved in producing an electric lamp had been reduced from 200 to 20 and the labour time from nearly an hour to 20 seconds. Not surprisingly the price of a carbon filament electric lamp over this period fell to less than 20 per cent of its original price.

1.4.11 Diffusion and suppression

diffusion

adoption of an innovation over time from limited use to widespread use in the market

As an innovation becomes accepted by an increasing number of individual and organisational users it goes through the process of diffusion, which is the process of adoption of an innovation over time from limited use to widespread use in the market.

From its original installation within the grounds of Edison's Menlo Park laboratory in late 1879, his system of electric lighting was installed in increasing numbers of individual factory and textile mill installations, and urban street lighting. This included the fulfilment of one of his visions when his electric light system started operating in the Pearl Street district of lower Manhattan in 1882 (Figure 21). His system gradually eclipsed its rivals and diffused into widespread use in commercial, civic and domestic situations.

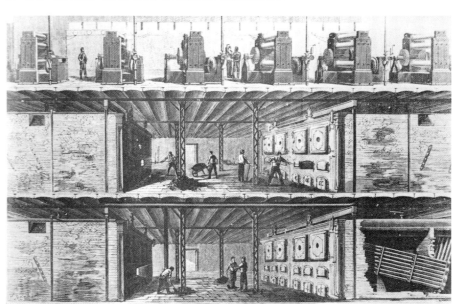

Figure 21   Interior of the Pearl Street generating station, 1882
Source: Smithsonian Institute

By the end of June the installation of equipment in the Pearl Street station was completed and the boilers were fired up. The first dynamo was started on 5 July and other equipment was tested during the rest of the month. On 4 September the first lights powered by Edison's electrical system were switched on.

suppression

delayed adoption of an innovation in the early years of its availability when it may compete with a dominant design

As you saw above with the example of the telephone there are also factors that can lead to suppression or delayed adoption of an innovation in the early years of its availability when it may compete with a dominate design.

First of all there may be patent disputes over the ownership of the invention. These can delay widespread sales until it becomes clear who has the right to market the innovation. Then for the duration of the patent other inventors are discouraged from devising improvements when they can't benefit from them.

There are also those individuals and companies currently providing technology and products that might be threatened by a newcomer, like telegraph companies faced with the telephone. They can sometimes use their power and influence to make it difficult for the new product to succeed – from influencing government legislation to outright sabotage. Then there's also a certain degree of protective inertia in business and institutional structures that tends to resist change in order to allow innovation to be absorbed in a steady evolutionary way rather than a more disruptive revolution.

Once an innovation has achieved widespread diffusion so that most of its market has been captured and the dominant design has had incremental improvement until it is relatively stable or mature, then one of two things usually happens. Either the mature innovation continues to sell with only minor modifications, unchallenged by any serious competition, or a radical new invention is devised that sets off another cycle of the innovation process to challenge what already exists.

1.4.12 Compact fluorescents and new developments

In the case of the electric light there were a series of incremental product innovations (metal filaments, gas filled bulbs, frosted bulbs) as well as process innovations (some of which were mentioned above), which steadily improved performance and reduced price until, by the 1930s, the incandescent light was mature and diffused in many nations.

Then in the mid-1930s a new invention appeared that was to challenge the incandescent lamp – the fluorescent lamp. This was the culmination of around 70 years' research into fluorescence (the conversion of one kind of light into another). In the modern fluorescent light a heated electrode emits electrons into a tube of mercury vapour causing the vapour to emit ultraviolet light, which is invisible to the human eye. This causes the phosphor coating on the inside of the tube to emit visible white light. Another cycle of innovation was under way when the new lamp was first introduced commercially in 1938.

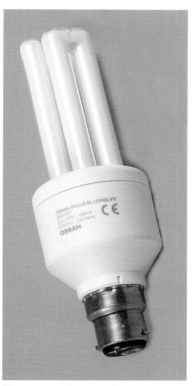

Figure 22   Domestic compact fluorescent lamp, 2005

Gradually the fluorescent light began to encroach on the market captured by the incandescent lamp, first in the workplace and then increasingly in the home, especially after the introduction of compact fluorescent lamps (CFLs) onto the domestic market in the 1980s (Figure 22). Compact fluorescents last 10 times as long as incandescents and use 20 per cent of the electricity. By 2004, with the unit cost falling, CFLs had broken through the 10 per cent barrier achieving the status of having a substantial market share (10–20 per cent) rather than being a niche market (over 1 per cent). Some projections expect them to achieve a 15 per cent share by 2010. This would still not be sufficient for CFLs to achieve the ultimate status of becoming the industry norm or the dominant brand.

Box 1 Race for the future of lighting

The problem with filament bulbs like those made by Edison and his successors is that they generate more heat than light – only about 10 per cent of the electricity becomes light – and turning them on and off shortens their life. The next generation of electric light is under development at the moment, based on more recent scientific discoveries and more advanced technological applications. But will it be one technology that wins or will several find their own niches in the lighting market? Along with fluorescent lighting there are currently (2005) at least two other competing technologies.

Electrodeless induction lamps

In the early 1990s an invention was revealed that might be the subject of the next cycle of lighting innovation – electrodeless induction lamps. The device, from a small Californian firm, Intersource Technologies, used a magnetic coil to generate radio waves that excited gases in the lamp, causing the phosphorous-coated interior surface of the glass cover to glow. The company estimated that the operational life of the lamp would be 15 000 to 20 000 operating hours, compared with 750 to 1000 hours for a conventional incandescent lamp. Without a filament or electrode, lamp failure is most likely to be due to the gradual degradation of the gas. Repair would then require the replacement of the glass cover only, rather than the expensive base and electronic components, making the system even cheaper to run.

Further electrodeless lamps were subsequently developed by Philips (QL system, Figure 23), General Electric (Genura) and Fusion Lighting (Solar 1000 sulfur lamp).

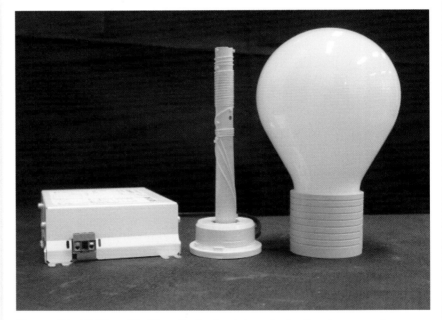

Figure 23 Philips QL 85-watt electrodeless induction lamp system
Source: Philips Lighting BV

Although all of these lamps have proved significantly longer lasting than incandescent and compact fluorescent lamps (for example Philips claims 100 000 hours for the QL), there are several factors that explain why we aren't all using them in our homes at the moment. They are all being tested in different environments and technical improvements made in response to the users' feedback – in other words the technology is still being developed and hasn't reached a stable enough state for mass manufacture. Current small-scale manufacture also means that the unit cost of existing versions of these lamps is high. In fact Philips' QL and Fusion's lamp are complete systems rather than replacement bulbs and are expensive on first installation. High purchase prices mean the product isn't taken up by consumers on a large enough scale to ensure its commercial success and to enable manufacturers to reduce prices.

So this technology is stuck in the vicious circle common to many innovations. Some of the companies developing these new lamps are hoping for assistance from government legislation on energy efficiency. Pierre Villere, chairman of Intersource, hopes the US government's Energy Policy Act will provide the incentive needed to interest buyers. Villere thinks, 'We will see ... the same thing happen in high-efficiency lighting that we saw in terms of safety and emission control in the automobile industry' (quoted in Rensselaer Polytechnic Institute, 1998).

White LEDs

Light-emitting diodes (LEDs) are devices that generate light when electrons pass between two kinds of semiconducting material. Normally the diodes emit a single colour depending on the amount of energy an electron is losing during its transition. You will be familiar with LEDs used in the displays of digital clocks, watches, and electrical appliances. They're also used in remote controls (emitting infrared light) and increasingly in car brake lights, traffic lights and giant TV screens. They convert about 90 per cent of their energy input into light and are very hard-wearing.

The challenge has been to find a way of getting LEDs to make white light for general-purpose use. One approach, first adopted by the Nichia Corporation of Japan in 1996, has been to coat the inside of the light bulb with a phosphorescent coating that gives off white light when hit by the LED's particular wavelength. But the phosphor wears over time – present (2005) estimates are for a 100 000-hour life. Another solution is to try to mix the appropriate primary colours but it's more difficult to make blue light than red and getting the balance right is difficult. However solutions have been found and the devices are being improved. White LEDs are being used in some specialised products such as torches and cave lamps.

As with the electrodeless lamps above, the technical performance of white LEDs is steadily improving and their cost is coming down as the price of semiconductor devices has fallen. However they are still much more expensive than incandescent and fluorescent lights, although arguably cheaper over the lifetime of a typical bulb. In 2003 the UK gadgets company EFX launched a range of white LED downlighters to replace halogen lighting for domestic and commercial use. EFX is using the slogan 'Global lighting to halt global warming'.

By the time you read this the situation will have moved on and its outcome may be clearer. Or maybe a completely different technical solution will have emerged – that's the nature of the innovation process.

1.4.13 Intellectual property and patents

At any stage of the innovation process, from invention to diffusion, a bright idea with market potential can be a target for unscrupulous copying. Or, as you've seen with simultaneous invention, people might be working on similar ideas in parallel and the origins of inventive ideas might be difficult to identify with precision. So it is sensible for inventors to establish their claim to a particular invention and to protect it against unauthorised exploitation by others.

There are different forms of legal protection to guard against the copying of intellectual property. The concept of intellectual property allows people to own and control the results of their creativity and ingenuity in the same way they own physical property. The most well known of these is the patent, which is an intellectual property right relating to inventions. It gives a right to stop others from exploiting the invention without permission.

intellectual property

patents, trademarks, designs and copyright allow people to own and control the results of their creativity and ingenuity

patent

an intellectual property right relating to inventions giving a right to stop others from exploiting the invention without permission

Patents are a means by which inventors are granted, by the state, exclusive rights to make, use or sell a new invention for a limited period (16–20 years in most countries) in exchange for agreeing to make public the details of their invention. The word patent comes from the Latin *litterae patentes*, meaning open letters, as in an official document that was open to inspection by all. The patent secures for the inventor a temporary monopoly protected by law and the state secures an addition to the body of technological knowledge that encourages further invention, technological progress and wealth creation.

A patent application is required to contain a description of the invention and the reasoning that led to it in sufficient detail to enable it to be reproduced by a third party. It often contains background information on previous related technology (known as prior art). Therefore patents provide an enormous amount of technical information that is used by many individuals and companies (Figure 24).

Once granted a patent gives an invention the legal status of personal property that can be sold or bequeathed to heirs of the inventor. In addition the owner of a patent may authorise others to make, use or sell the invention in exchange for royalties or other compensation.

According to the UK Patent Office (**www.patent.gov.uk**), to be granted a patent an inventor's product or process must satisfy four criteria.

1   It must be new – the idea must never have been disclosed publicly in any way, anywhere, prior to the claim being filed.

2   It must involve an inventive step – the idea must not be obvious to someone with a good knowledge and experience of the subject.

3   It must be capable of industrial application – it must take the physical form of a substance, product or apparatus, or of an industrial type of process.

4   It must not be excluded – an invention is not patentable if it is of a type listed as specifically excluded, although such lists vary in different countries.

In 2005 the UK exclusions were:

- a discovery

- a scientific theory or mathematical method

- an aesthetic creation – literary, dramatic or artistic work

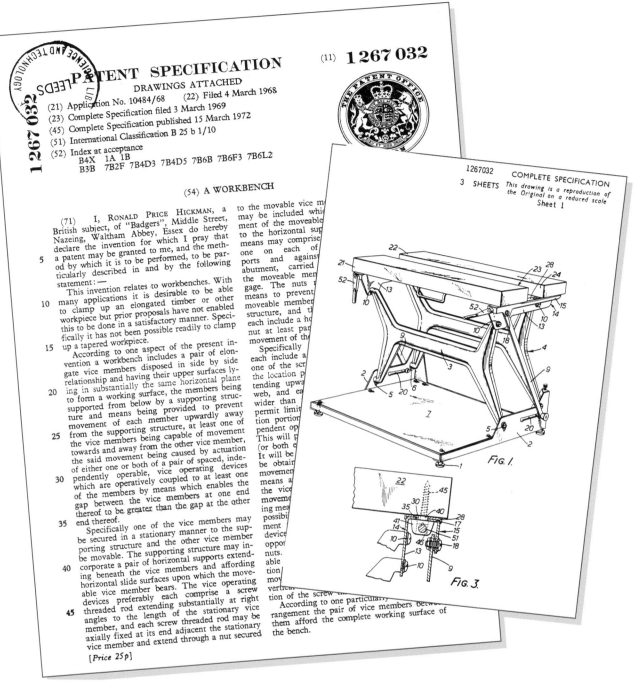

Figure 24 Extracts from the patent for the novel features of the Workmate portable workbench Source: Patent Specification 1267032 'A Workbench'

- a scheme or method for performing a mental act, playing a game or doing business – unless it has physical features such as special apparatus

- the presentation of information, or a computer program

- a new animal or plant variety, a method of treatment of the human or animal body by surgery or therapy, or a method of diagnosis.

While in the UK you cannot patent computer programmes, new plant varieties or human DNA, patenting is allowed on some of those categories of invention in the USA. Europe and the UK are coming under increasing pressure to adopt US practice.

There are other forms of protection for intellectual property. The design features that distinguish one product from another can be protected by means of registered designs. Sketches and drawings for a new product can be protected by design right, which is an extension to copyright that protects an artistic or literary creation. Words or symbols that are used to distinguish goods or services from rivals in a similar field can be protected by trade and service marks.

Edison was a great believer in the patent system and over his lifetime was granted more than 1000 patents. However there is a dilemma for individuals and companies considering patenting. Once granted, copies of the patent application are publicly available.

It has been known for unscrupulous companies to manufacture an invention without permission from the patent holder. Sometimes this occurs after an inventor has shown a company an invention in an attempt to persuade them to invest in it. Sometimes copying occurs after launch when a rival company might reverse engineer a promising innovation and produce its own version. Individual inventors are particularly susceptible to this kind of treatment as patenting is expensive, especially if worldwide protection is needed, and the only means of defending patent rights, if they have been infringed, is through the courts.

While large companies might be in a position to take such legal action few individuals can afford it. Rare examples include Edison and Bell, and more recently Ron Hickman and James Dyson. Ron Hickman, the inventor of the Workmate portable workbench, spent more than £1 million in fighting infringements of his patents as part of his agreement with Black & Decker, to whom he had licensed production of his invention. And in 2000, James Dyson sued Hoover whose Triple Vortex bagless cleaner was held to infringe Dyson's 1980 patent for his cyclone cleaner.

In order to avoid the problem of infringement some companies choose not to patent but rather to keep their invention secret from competitors. This way they hope to benefit from being 'first to market' with a new product and capture a large market share before their competitors come up with a rival product. (There's more on this and other corporate innovation strategies in Section 3.) Because of reverse engineering it's harder to keep product inventions secret compared with new processes. You'll see in a later example that the company 3M chose not to patent the new machines it invented to manufacture its Post-it adhesive note pads though it did patent the pads themselves.

1.5   Dead certs and dead ends

Most of us have some experience of the evolutionary development and the success of new technology. The Walkman personal stereo cassette player has evolved into the Discman CD player and more recently into digital music players. The computer has developed from its beginnings as government and university research machines in the 1940s (the first electronic computer filled an entire room and had a memory of

16 kilobytes) to palm-sized personal digital assistants each one of which has more computing power than that used in the Apollo moon landings. The mobile phone has become one of the fastest spreading innovations in history, going from less than 5 per cent ownership in the UK in 1990 to more than 70 per cent by 2003.

But these successes are only the tip of the innovation iceberg. For every product, successful or not, which reaches the market there are many more that never get that far. It has been estimated that no more than 2 per cent of inventions go on to become innovations. And for every successful innovative product there are many that do not achieve commercial success and are eventually (or quickly) withdrawn.

Can you think of examples?

I can think of the Sinclair C5 vehicle, the laser disk, Betamax video cassettes and the 8-track audio cartridge.

Yet the urge to invent remains strong and the commercial rewards of success can be spectacular. There are almost 5 million patents currently in force worldwide. More than 1 million new patent applications are made each year – almost 500 000 of these each year by the Japanese alone. In addition there are many more inventions worldwide that are not patented.

In Section 2 I'll look at what motivates people to invent and at how they do it.

Box 2   Are cylinder ships a dead-end invention?

In 1924 Anton Flettner, a German physicist, tested a prototype of one of his inventions, a rotor ship. An expert in hydrodynamics and aerodynamics, Flettner had already experimented with metal sails, which he found increased sailing ship efficiency by 50 per cent. Next he moved on to an ingenious application of the Magnus effect – the idea that a sphere or cylinder spinning in an airstream develops a force at right angles to the moving air. This theory was developed to account for inaccuracies in the flight of cannonballs but the effect is more recognisable today as being responsible for the swerving of golf, tennis and soccer balls when hit with a slice.

Flettner discovered that when the wind blew at right-angles onto rotating cylinders a vacuum was created ahead of the cylinder and an area of high pressure behind, resulting in forward propulsion. Experiments showed that a rotating cylinder could extract up to 15 times as much energy from the wind as the same area of sail.

In an attempt to demonstrate the promise of such a technology Flettner converted a 680-tonne ship, the *Buckau* (Figure 25a), replacing her masts and rigging with two hollow cylindrical towers made of sheet iron. The cylinders were 20 metres high and 3 metres in diameter, and were rotated at 120 rpm by small electric motors at their base, driven in turn by a small diesel engine. In addition to being able to extract more energy from the wind the cylinders were lighter than rigging and sails and had a lower centre of gravity, making the ship more stable and manoeuvrable. A further advantage over conventional sailing ships was that the *Buckau* was less susceptible to sudden squalls and therefore could sail through strong winds where an ordinary sailing vessel would have to take down its sails. As a result it could be faster and fewer crew members were needed to control the rotors compared with sails.

Results of the trials with the *Buckau* suggested that substitution of rotors for sails in vessels up to 3000 tonnes was a practical possibility. The Hamburg-Amerika line ordered 10 rotor ships but only one, the *Barbara*, was built. In 1926 Flettner, having renamed his ship the *Baden-Baden* (Figure 25b), successfully crossed the Atlantic in an attempt to publicise and gain support for his invention.

Flettner had suggested that rotors could be added to all steam or marine diesel-powered vessels to reduce expenditure on coal and oil. However at the time there was an abundance of cheap fuel that reduced the strength of this advantage. In addition the ships developed serious mechanical problems because of the constant vibration of the rotors and they still relied on wind for this type of propulsion. So at the time rotors did not offer a significant advantage over existing technologies, they merely offered added complexity and unreliability. Less than 20 years after their invention the last of these potentially revolutionary new ships had been broken up for scrap.

During the oil crises of the 1970s the idea was briefly revised and more recently found expression in the Cousteau Society's expedition ship, *Alcyone* (Figure 26). Built in 1985 the *Alcyone* uses two fixed cylinders with movable shutters and fans to achieve the same 'lift' produced by Flettner's more cumbersome rotors. When combined with modern computer control that switches between the Turbosail and the ship's engines according to the state of the wind, this system allows for a 35 per cent saving in fossil-fuel use.

So this invention might not be the technological dead-end it appeared to be with the demise of Flettner's ships. Indeed as fossil fuels become more scarce and expensive there's every chance that cylinder technology might be taken up again on a larger scale.

Figure 25(a) Anton Flettner's rotor ship, the *Buckau*. This prototype proved the principle of propulsion from the effect of wind hitting two rotating hollow towers. Source: Corbis/Hulton Deutsch Collection

Figure 25(b) The *Baden-Baden* arriving in New York from Hamburg in 1926. The ship caused a sensation in the USA. Source: Hulton Archive

Figure 26 The Cousteau Society's expedition ship, *Alcyone*, built in 1985 Source: Science Photo Library

The *Alcyone* uses Turbosail technology. A fan draws air into each of its two 10-metre-tall cylindrical masts. This creates forward lift that surpasses that attained by a normal sail, and reduces the ship's fuel consumption by a third.

Self-assessment questions

Each section contains self-assessment questions to test your understanding. The answers are after the last section.

SAQ 1

Given the definitions above, would you classify the following as an invention or an innovation?

(a) BIC ballpoint pen

(b) Flettner's rotor ship

(c) Edison's tinfoil phonograph

(d) Edison's bamboo-filament light bulb.

SAQ 2

Would you classify the following as examples of radical innovation or incremental innovation?

(a) Edison's phonograph

(b) compact fluorescent lamps

(c) Edison's electric light

(d) Bell's telephone.

SAQ 3

What are the four criteria that must be satisfied for an inventor to be granted a patent on an invention?

Key points of Section 1

- Invention and innovation are ongoing processes not one-off events. Products have a history of invention, design and improvement, which can be over a surprisingly long period.

- It can be difficult to identify a product's original inventor. Often different people are working on developing a technology simultaneously.

- It can take imagination to foresee how a new technology might be used, particularly for potential financial backers.

- To succeed an innovation needs a competitive advantage over existing technologies or products.

- Research and experiment into one technology can contribute to the development of another spin-off technology.

- Innovative products can take time to become widely used. However in recent years the timescales for diffusion have shortened.

- The success of an innovation depends on regular improvements to its performance, reliability and design coupled with price reduction. This is usually achieved by further innovations in supporting technology, manufacturing processes, component performance, new materials, and so on.

- A group of early, sometimes specialised users of an innovation can play an important part in giving momentum to its sales.

- Affordability of innovative products is linked to the cost of manufacture and the relative affluence of buyers.

- There are also fashions in innovative products – shaped by marketing and advertising – which can stimulate demand. Cultural factors can also have an influence on innovation and consumption.

- As an innovation spreads it may change from being a novelty or luxury to a necessity for people.

- Governments can affect the environment for innovation in particular areas of technology, which can lead to lower prices and the faster introduction of an innovation. Accordingly political and regulatory factors can play a part in the innovation process.

- To be granted the protection of a patent an invention must be new, involve an inventive step, be capable of industrial application and not excluded.

- There are factors that can suppress or delay the spread of an innovation – patent disputes over ownership; resistance from people with a vested interest in established technologies; protective inertia in business and institutional structures resisting radical change.

The key points for Section 1 meet learning outcomes 1.1, 1.2, 1.3, 1.4, 2.1, 2.2, 2.3 and 3.1.

2 Invention

Having taken a broad look at the whole innovation process from invention to diffusion, I'll go back and look more closely at what motivates individuals and organisations to invent. Then I'll consider how people generate ideas for inventions and the designs based on the inventions.

2.1 How invention starts

It seems clear from the number of new patents applied for each year, and the many inventions that are not patented, that the level of inventive activity around the world is high. It's possible to identify a number of starting points for invention and new product development. For the purposes of this analysis I'll consider first what motivates individuals to invent and then what drives invention in organisations.

2.1.1 What motivates individuals to invent?

While economic incentives are behind the development and commercialisation of most innovations, most inventions are the product of inventors' individual interests and motivations, creative thought processes and personal make-up.

Individuals invent usually because they have:

- scientific or technical curiosity

- constructive discontent

- desire to make money

- desire to help others.

Scientific or technical curiosity

Some inventors understand a scientific phenomenon and set about inventing a technological device to exploit the phenomenon.

The invention of the laser grew from the interest of two researchers in studying the structure and characteristics of a variety of molecules. During the Second World War Charles H. Townes worked on developing radar navigation bombing systems. After the war he had the idea of modifying the radar techniques and using microwaves to study molecular structure. Subsequently he and Arthur L. Schawlow collaborated at Bell Labs in the USA on using the shorter wavelengths of infrared and optical light to develop an even more powerful tool – the laser (short for light amplification by stimulated emission of radiation). They were granted a patent in 1960. However they had no thoughts about any applications of their invention other than its use in their scientific research. Schawlow recalled:

> We thought it might have some communications and scientific uses, but we had no application in mind. If we had, it might have hampered us and not worked out as well.
>
> (Bell Labs, 1998)

It was left to others to devise ways of exploiting this invention in a commercial product. Although initially perceived by some as a weapon (a death ray), one of the first practical applications was in medicine for eye surgery. Lasers have gone on to have widespread use in industry for cutting and welding, in commerce for bar code readers, at home for

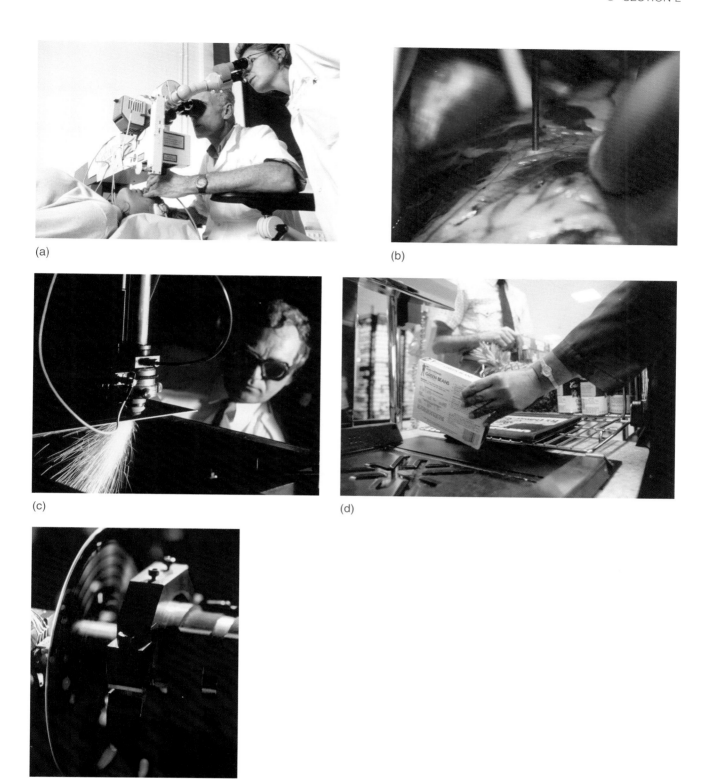

(a)

(b)

(c)

(d)

(e)

Figure 27   Originally developed for scientific research into the structure of molecules, the laser now has a huge range of applications. (a) Laser surgery to correct short-sightedness Source: Science Photo Library. **(b) Laser heart surgery** Source: Science Photo Library. **(c) Industrial carbon dioxide laser cutting metal** Source: Science Photo Library. **(d) Bar-code reader at supermarket checkout** Source: Science Photo Library. **(e) A laser beam is creating a digital track of information on a master disc. The master disc is then used to mass-produce CDs. The information will be read off a CD in a domestic player by using a similar laser beam.** Source: Science Photo Library.

entertainment (CD players, DVD players), in data storage and retrieval in computers, and so on (Figure 27). The world market for laser technology is now over $100 billion a year.

Inventions can arise from the technical curiosity of creative individuals rather than to meet a clear need. There are many examples, particularly in the past but still occasionally nowadays, of so-called talented tinkerers. Read Box 3 for an account of what talented tinkering can produce.

Box 3   Talented tinkering and the hovercraft

Christopher Cockerell was an electrical engineer who left the Marconi company to become a boat builder in Norfolk. He developed an interest in increasing boat speed by reducing friction between the hull and the water. He had the idea of supporting a craft on a low-pressure cushion of air contained within a high-pressure curtain of air (Figure 28). He built a mock-up to test his idea using a cat food tin inside a coffee tin connected to a vacuum cleaner reversed to blow, all mounted above a set of kitchen scales to measure the pressure exerted (Figure 29). It was three times the pressure of the blower without the tins and confirmed his theory. There had been previous attempts to build a vehicle that floated on air but Cockerell was the first to devise a way of containing the air cushion. Next he constructed a radio-controlled balsa wood model of his hovercraft to prove the hover principle would work in practice (Figure 30).

Cockerell applied for a patent in 1955. The Patent Office didn't know whether to classify it as a boat or a plane. The Ministry of Supply was similarly confused when Cockerell demonstrated his model but it immediately classified the invention as secret. It was only after Cockerell discovered the Swiss were working on a similar device that the ministry agreed it could be declassified and commercialised.

Having persuaded the National Research Development Corporation to back the hovercraft, the first full-size manned prototype SR-N1 was built by Saunders Roe in 1959 and crossed the English Channel in July of that year (Figure 31). It soon became apparent that the peripheral jet on the SR-N1 didn't provide enough lift to make it a practical form of transport. Cockerell devised and patented a flexible skirt to retain the air cushion. A series of experimental hovercraft designs for both civil and military applications followed the SR-N1. In 1962 the first passenger-carrying scheduled service started up across the estuary of the river Dee in north Wales and cross-channel services began in 1966 (Figure 32).

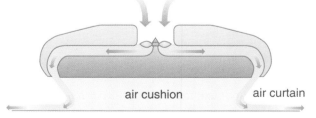

air cushion   air curtain

Figure 28   Cockerell's peripheral jet hovercraft principle

Figure 29 Mock-up from empty tins, a vacuum cleaner and kitchen scales used to test the hover principle Source: Hovercraft Museum Trust

Figure 30 Christopher Cockerell with the first proper Hovercraft model made in 1955 from balsa wood Source: Hovercraft Consultants Ltd

Although there are still commercial and military hovercraft in operation (Figure 33), high development costs, technical problems and cheaper competing technologies have meant they did not go on to become widely used. Rather they are used in specific situations where their ability to cross varied surfaces inaccessible to conventional vehicles gives them an advantage.

Figure 31 World's first full-size hovercraft. The prototype SR-N1 was used for research and development. Source: Science & Society Picture Library

Figure 32 Commercial cross-channel hovercraft landing at Dieppe
Source: Science Photo Library

Cockerell resigned from Hovercraft Development Ltd after a dispute and the UK government persuaded him to sell his patent for £150 000 in 1971. He continued to work as an inventor, including designing a system of rafts to generate electricity from waves, but never really profited from his inventions. He had devised 36 inventions worth millions of pounds for Marconi and was paid £10 for each one. The money he received for his hovercraft patent didn't cover his development costs. Unsurprisingly he remained bitter at what is characterised as the UK's repeated failure to capitalise on the inventive ideas of creative individuals. There is more about this in Section 4.

Figure 33   US naval hovercraft are still in use Source: Textron Systems

Figure 34   Dyson's Ballbarrow. The ball-shaped wheel improves the ride over rough or soft ground. Source: courtesy of Dyson Ltd

Constructive discontent

Inventive ideas often arise because existing technology or design proves to be unsatisfactory in some way – perhaps too costly, too inefficient or too dangerous. Using a product or process for a while can reveal inadequacies in its performance and is often vital preparation for producing ideas for improvements. You may have become dissatisfied either with an existing product or process or with the fact that something doesn't exist to meet a need you've identified. But creative individuals go further than this unfocused dissatisfaction and actually try to do something about it.

James Dyson became dissatisfied with the wheel of a conventional wheelbarrow sinking into sand and soft soil so in 1974 he re-invented the wheel. His Ballbarrow is designed with a ball-shaped wheel to ride over soft ground without sinking and to absorb the shock when used on rough ground (Figure 34). It also has feet that don't sink in the mud and a plastic bin that doesn't rust – both drawbacks of previous wheelbarrows he'd used.

Box 4 Constructive discontent and the invention of photocopying

In the early 1930s, US patent lawyer Chester Carlson began to be dissatisfied with existing methods of copying patents that he required for his work. He was determined to find a better means than the existing photographic methods, which were slow and inefficient.

After an extensive search through patents and other literature he identified some promising ideas. He began experimenting and in 1938 produced the first print using a process that eventually was to become the basis of the modern photocopier (Figure 35).

Figure 35   Chester Carlson, the inventor of xerography, with his first xerographic apparatus Source: Rank Xerox UK Ltd

Static electricity was the key to his invention. Carlson started with a sulfur-coated plate, though later this was developed into a selenium drum, which was given an overall negative electrical charge. An image of a document was then projected or reflected onto the charged surface. The charge was removed where the light struck the surface, leaving only the dark part of the image such as text characters negatively charged. Positively charged particles of dry powder were then applied that stuck to the negatively charged portions of the plate or drum. The powder was then transferred to paper and fused on to it by heating, leaving a permanent image.

In his 1939 patent Carlson called this process electrophotography (Figure 36). But he soon came to call it xerography – from the Greek xeros meaning dry and graphein, meaning to write.

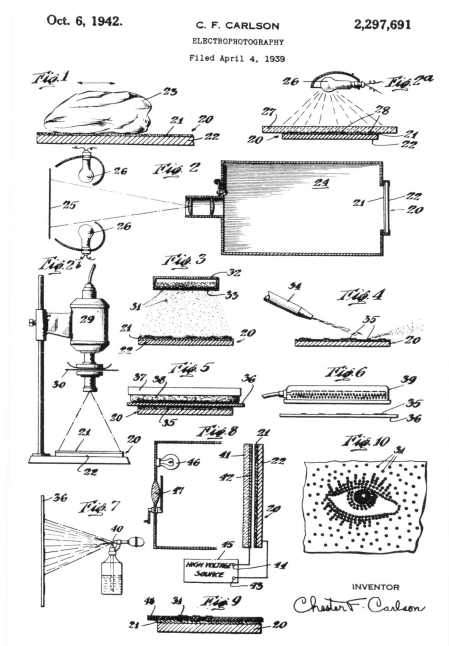

Oct. 6, 1942.   C. F. CARLSON   2,297,691
ELECTROPHOTOGRAPHY
Filed April 4, 1939

Figure 36   Extract from Chester Carlson's 1939 patent application on electrophotography, which established the essential principles of photocopying Source: van Dulken, 2002

His invention was a radical departure from existing technology, however, and it took many years both to develop and improve the invention and to persuade a company to invest in it. In 1944 the Battelle Memorial Institute, a non-profit-making organisation, agreed to finance the invention and after a few years of development signed an agreement with a small photographic materials company, the Haloid Corporation, to market the invention.

The first electrostatic copier, the Haloid 1385, came onto the market in the late 1940s. It was manually operated and took several minutes to make each copy. Not surprisingly it was not successful at first because it did not offer an advantage over existing methods of copying, which by this time were a combination of carbon paper for a small number of copies and electromechanical stencil duplicators for a larger volume.

Finally, after another decade of effort at improving the technology, the first automatic, plain-paper photocopier the Xerox 914 was launched onto the market in 1959 – Haloid had changed its name to Xerox. This was an automatic machine that operated at the push of a button and could produce seven copies a minute. It was the foundation for a huge multibillion dollar business in which Xerox, thanks to its patents, had a monopoly until the late 1980s.

When the patent protection expired, rivals, mainly Japanese, began to enter this lucrative market in competition with Xerox. The original fairly straightforward need has been cultivated by what the ever-improving technology has made possible – monochrome copiers producing a hundred copies a minute and capable of collating, stapling, enlarging and reducing. The colour photocopier was brought out in 1973 and the laser colour copier in 1986.

Now it is impossible to imagine a modern office without photocopying facilities. Xerox also took advantage of the increasing use of computing in the office to diversify into computer printers, scanners, fax machines and multifunction machines. Many people predicted that the spread of computers would lead to the paperless office. However recent estimates suggest people are making 500 billion photocopies each year, and 15 trillion (15 000 000 000 000) copies on photocopiers, computer printers and multifunction machines combined in the USA alone (Lyman and Varian, 2003).

Cat's-eyes and road conditions

Sometimes the discontent comes from the fact that there isn't a product to satisfy a particular need. Percy Shaw was a road mender who was aware of the dangers of driving along unlit, often fog-bound, roads. One night in 1933 he was driving his car near his home in the north of England when his headlights were reflected in the eyes of a cat. This inspired him to invent the cat's-eye reflector that, when embedded at intervals in the centre of the road, reflected a vehicle's headlights and made it easier to pick out and follow the course of the road (Figure 37).

With hindsight the need and the solution seem self-evident – like many ingenious ideas. But Shaw's act of insight was to recognise the need and work out a means by which it could be met.

Seventy years after Shaw's invention a new generation of cat's-eyes have been developed and have been tested in sites around the UK and several other countries. Called intelligent road studs, they have a built-in microprocessor and sensors that can detect different weather conditions as well as the speed of passing traffic (Figure 38). They are powered by a solar cell feeding a rechargeable battery.

In addition to passively reflecting light up to 80 metres, the studs can actively project light of different colours that is detectable at up to 1000 metres. When a stud detects fog it can emit a flashing white light. When it detects a significant drop in temperature it can emit blue light to indicate the possibility of ice. In a hazardous situation studs can leave a trail of orange lights behind passing vehicles to warn against following too closely. Studs can even communicate with each other so that, for instance, a vehicle detected on the wrong side of the road can trigger red warning lights in studs on the other side of a blind hill or corner.

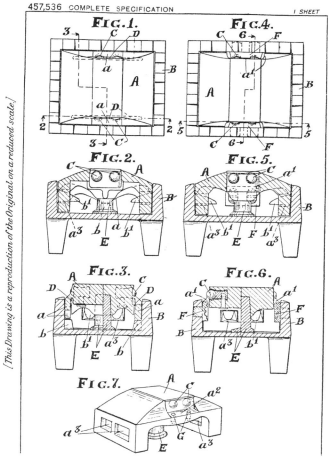

Figure 37 **Extract from the patent for cat's-eyes – an example of a highly successful patent for a simple but ingenious idea. 'FIG.6.' shows how a rubber insert (part 'F') cleans the lenses when they are depressed by a passing vehicle.** Source: van Dulken, 2002

Desire to make money

While most inventors might dream of growing rich from their inventions few invent for that reason alone. There are some exceptions though.

Take the case of the safety razor. One person, a travelling salesman named King Camp Gillette, was primarily responsible for the original invention and prototype. Unlike many lone inventors Gillette was not inventing something arising from a hobby or a field of technology with which he was already familiar. He was deliberately searching for a winner. He'd been advised by William Painter, the inventor of the disposable crown cork bottle cap, to try to invent a disposable product for which the consumer would develop a continuing need, guaranteeing a steady market for the innovation.

In 1895 while shaving with his cut-throat razor Gillette realised that the edge of the razor was the key to shaving. He had the bright idea of dividing the components into a handle and holder for a disposable blade. The blade could then be thrown away when blunt, avoiding the need for regular sharpening. However his limited practical skills could take the invention no further than the prototype stage. To make further progress Gillette obtained the help of William Nickerson, the inventor of the push-button elevator control mechanism. Nickerson worked on refining the razor and on improving the process of sharpening the steel blades.

(a)   (b)

Figure 38   (a) These intelligent road studs not only reflect but can also actively project light of different colours. (b) Intelligent road studs being tested on a public road. Source: courtesy of Reflector Ltd

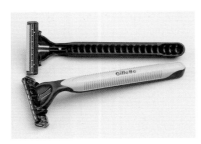

Figure 39   Recent Gillette safety razors with disposable blades

Gillette's safety razor finally went on sale in 1903. With only the very edge of the blade exposed to the skin it was far safer than the old cut-throat razor. Furthermore beards were becoming less popular so Gillette anticipated large sales. At first he was disappointed – in the first year he sold only 51 safety razors and 168 blades. In the following year though, sales took off – 90 000 razors and 12.5 million blades.

The Gillette company, based around the safety razor, went from strength to strength. It's a familiar and successful company 100 years on (Figure 39). Though still largely based around razors it has diversified slightly into so-called grooming products, toothbrushes and oral care, and into batteries. The concept of disposability still applies to many of its products. In 2002 it was the largest razor manufacturer in the world and its net sales were $8.45 billion.

Desire to help others

This is a less common motivation but it shows not everyone is driven by money.

In 1991 the inventor Trevor Baylis saw a BBC documentary about the spread of HIV/AIDS in Africa. What was needed was a way of broadcasting the safe-sex message to people in areas without electricity and where batteries for a radio could cost a month's wages. Solar power wouldn't necessarily help as most people who could get to a radio listened in the evening after work. While absorbing this information he imagined himself as a colonial administrator in the Sudan, sipping gin and listening to an old-fashioned wind-up gramophone.

Then Baylis had the inspired thought that if a simple clockwork spring could power a gramophone then it could be applied to a spring-driven radio. Months of experimentation eventually produced a prototype of a hand-cranked clockwork mechanism that drove a tiny generator that powered a radio for 14 minutes on a 30-second wind. After a 4-year period of fund-raising, market research, design and development, the first Freeplay radio was launched in 1995 (Figure 40).

Figure 40   Baylis's original Freeplay wind-up radio, 1995 Source: Science & Society Picture Library

Later a solar panel was added to provide continuous play in sunlight and recharge an internal battery

For a number of years the radio was made by disabled workers in a factory in South Africa. Subsequently the manufacture of Freeplay products was transferred to China. However the spirit behind Trevor Baylis's invention has found an outlet in the Freeplay Foundation that, since 2000, has complemented the work of various agencies by distributing self-powered radios free as part of a range of humanitarian initiatives.

2.1.2   What drives invention in organisations?

Much invention and nearly all innovation nowadays take place inside organisations – from small start-up companies to well-established multinationals. This is mainly because increasingly invention and innovation require access to technology and resources beyond the scope of most individuals. But it is also because competitiveness and survival depend on the continual improvement of a company's products and processes. This provides a strong incentive for companies to invest in both the incremental improvement of existing products and the invention of new products.

Invention in organisations is usually driven by one or more of these:

- business strategy

- need to improve product or process

- opportunity offered by a new material, technology or manufacturing process

- government policy, legislation and regulations.

Business strategy

Invention can be driven by a company's business strategy. In descending order of inventiveness the main strategies are first to market, follow the leader, and opportunist.

First to market

Some companies have an offensive strategy in which they aim to be *first to market* with a new product. Such companies can be a major source of new products. This is risky as it requires a large investment in developing the product and cultivating the market before any return can be expected from sales. However it can be the most rewarding strategy, especially if the market can be sustained by continual incremental improvements to the product and the market share defended against competitors.

In the 1970s and 1980s Clive Sinclair's company Sinclair Research was first to market in the UK with a series of inventive products including pocket calculators, digital watches and home computers. For example the Sinclair ZX80 microcomputer, launched in 1980, was the first computer made to appeal to the mass market (Figure 41). Developed

Figure 41   Sinclair ZX80 microcomputer, 1980 Source: Science & Society Picture Library

as a build-it-yourself programmable computer, it was designed to connect to a television set and to a cassette recorder for loading programs. It was small and lightweight, weighing just 340 grams and was accessible to a wide sector of the population, being priced at just £99. All these characteristics made the Sinclair ZX80 the forerunner of a whole generation of personal computers. Its successor, the ZX81, had a better programming language called BASIC, fewer components, a simpler design and was £30 cheaper.

In 1982 the ZX Spectrum added colour, became the company's most significant commercial success and enabled Sinclair Research to achieve market dominance in the UK in the early 1980s. However the company was eventually out-performed by a number of companies that had followed it into the microcomputer market that Sinclair Research had helped to establish.

Follow the leader

Some companies have a defensive strategy and aim to *follow the leader*. Such companies hope to profit from the mistakes of the first-to-market company by devising incremental design and performance improvements and cost reductions compared with the original product. In addition they hope to exploit the new market that has started to grow, so timing is important. In the area of consumer electronics, for example, most of the inventions (radio, television, audio and video tape recording) were first brought to the market by European and US companies. But it was the major Japanese companies (such as Sony, JVC, Toshiba) that captured a large share of the mass market through reducing the cost of these devices and improving their performance.

The best of these companies were able to use the resources gained from being successful followers to then adopt a more offensive strategy and invent new products, such as Sony with the Walkman. Sony was first to market with this innovative product, which quickly became an important contributor to the company's profits. A number of companies followed Sony into this market with variations on the Walkman. However Sony had sufficient a head start to the extent that almost 25 years later it still had the largest market share in most areas of personal audio.

Interestingly the area it isn't performing in as well yet is the newest, the market for digital music players. Here it wasn't first to market and currently (2005) this market is dominated by a mixture of smaller companies and a few big companies that developed players before Sony.

Opportunist

Some companies have an *opportunist* strategy and aim to identify new market opportunities, needs and demands. Rather than developing new products though, the inventiveness of such companies lies in finding new outlets for existing products. UK examples include Sock Shop and Tie Rack from the 1980s, and more recently the small companies that have made a profit selling a variety of ring tones for mobile phones.

Need to improve product or process

Even though an invention will have been thoroughly tested before launch it's not possible for a company to test its performance in every situation in which it will be used. Real users are likely to discover how the product might not perform well or how it doesn't meet their needs. Once a company learns about these deficiencies it can address them through redesign. There are a number of incentives to do this: improve the product's performance in order to increase its appeal to larger numbers of buyers; further reduce materials and manufacturing costs to the company to increase profit; reduce the purchase price to promote sales.

This invention driver accounts for much incremental invention. You've already seen an example of this process in the development of the telephone – new components, new features, and spin-off inventions are all the result of attempts to improve existing technology.

An extreme example of this process was Sinclair Research, mentioned above. In the early 1970s it launched a range of electronic calculators that were designed to be small and light enough to fit in the pocket. For example the Cambridge calculator was sold both as a kit and fully built (Figure 42). Although at £29.95 it was expensive when first introduced, a year later the price had fallen to below £15. The Cambridge calculator was small, even by modern standards, weighing only 100 grams. However it suffered from a design flaw; after a certain amount of use the calculator was impossible to turn off due to oxidation of cheap components used in the switch contacts. Some critics say that Sinclair Research's innovative products were often launched prematurely and early buyers used as developmental testers. Feedback from these buyers was then used to make improvements to the products. While this undoubtedly led to improved products arguably it damaged the company's reputation as a supplier of reliable products and it was eventually edged out of the market by companies with more conventional business strategies.

I've already mentioned another, more conventional, example of incremental improvement. This was when Marcel Bich invented an improved manufacturing and assembly process to enable the BIC ballpoint pen to be manufactured on a large scale and for a significantly lower unit cost.

Opportunity offered by a new material, technology or manufacturing process

More often when new materials or technologies appear they are used to improve the performance of existing products. But in an increasing number of cases their appearance can make it possible to create new products.

New materials

The discovery of new materials, exploration of their properties and the invention of new industrial processes is a huge field of study in its own right. The potential rewards for a company discovering a successful application of a new material are great.

An example of this is shape memory alloys (SMAs). SMAs are mixtures of metals that, after being stress treated, can be deformed significantly but then triggered to return to their original shape. Some display unusual elastic properties and immediately spring back into shape, others recover their shape when heated. Originally made from an equal

Figure 42 Sinclair Cambridge electronic calculator, 1973
Source: Science & Society Picture Library

This model was one of a series of small calculators developed by the British inventor Sir Clive Sinclair in the early 1970s

combination of nickel and titanium – still the most common SMA – further experiments have led to many more SMAs combining two or more different metals. These remarkable memory properties have been applied to an increasing number of new or improved products. One of the most visible applications is in superelastic spectacles that can regain their shape after you've sat on them (Figure 43).

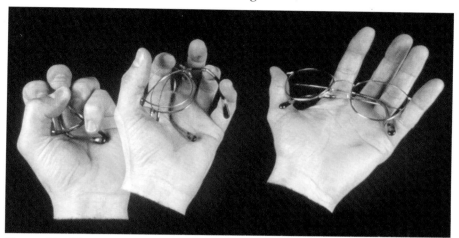

Figure 43   Shape memory alloy spectacles Source: Science Photo Library

There are currently dozens of other applications, particularly in the area of medical instruments. A stent is a tiny wire mesh tube used to reinforce weak arteries or to widen arteries narrowed by coronary heart disease (Figure 44). These are delivered to the heart in a catheter on the end of a wire usually inserted into an artery in the groin. Once in place they are expanded to their full size by inflating a balloon positioned inside the stent. However stents can now be made from SMAs and are stressed into a smaller diameter. When delivered by the catheter the stent expands to its intended size due to the heat of the body.

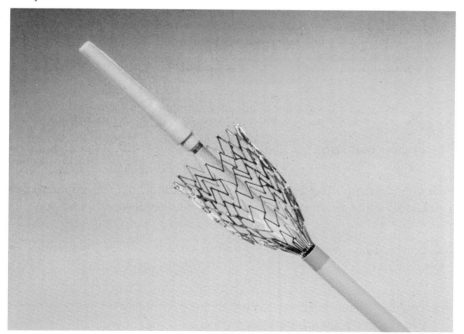

Figure 44   SMA stent that expands to its intended size when subjected to body temperature. These are predicted to replace stainless steel stents expanded with a balloon. Source: Nitinol Devices & Components Inc

New technology

The appearance of a new technology often results in the possibility of developing a whole range of new products. The invention of the transistor in the USA by Bardeen, Brattain and Shockley in 1947 led to a vast market of improved consumer electronics goods such as portable radios, hi-fi and television (Figure 45). Later on the related inventions of the integrated circuit in 1959 (by Jack St Clair Kilby at Texas instruments) and the microprocessor in 1971 (by Marcian E. Hoff at Intel) allowed the development of personal computers.

Figure 45   UK's first portable all-transistor radio, the Pam 710, was launched in 1956 Source: Science & Society Picture Library

It was a luxury item, costing roughly a month's wages, but the use of transistors led before long to miniature radios at affordable prices. Sound broadcasts could now be listened to anywhere.

Increasing miniaturisation and the improved computing capacity of microprocessors has permitted the addition of electronic components to many new products and processes. Examples are all around: palm-size mobile phones, programmable timing devices in electrical equipment, TV and video remote controllers. This trend is heading towards the invention of a growing range of new intelligent products that can store information about themselves and communicate with their environment (see Box 5).

Box 5   Radio frequency identification tags

RFID tags can be attached to individual products and can contain detailed information about that product such as its constituents, price, date of manufacture and so on. There's a confident prediction that by 2012 RFID tags will have replaced barcodes. This is given credence by the fact that in June 2003 the Wal-mart retail company announced that it would require all its suppliers to put RFID tags on all products by 2005.

And Tesco announced that it would introduce RFID into its entire supply chain by 2007.

There are three main components of an RFID tag system:

- A tag comprises electronic circuitry and an antenna (Figure 46). The tag acts as a data store and a wireless transponder that sends information about that product in response to interrogation from a reader.

- A reader transmits and receives signals.

- A computer system processes the information it receives from the reader.

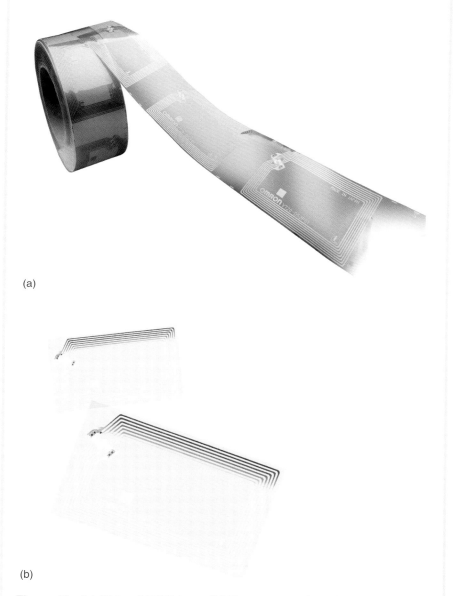

(a)

(b)

Figure 46 (a) Strip of RFID tags. (b) Two tags ready to be attached to products. Source: Omron Electronics Ltd

RFID tags are more robust than barcodes because they can suffer some damage and still be read. Another advantage is they don't require direct line-of-sight contact with readers, in fact some tags can be read from distances of several tens of metres and through obstructions. As well as passive RFID tags there are also active tags with their own power supply that allows product data to be modified and increases the transmission distance significantly.

RFID tags were first used in stock control and ordering, and in inventory checking. Products can be tracked as they move from factory to storeroom to shelf, reducing losses of stock in the supply chain and increasing the accuracy of restocking. In some systems, so-called smart shelves read the RFID signals from individual products and when stock runs low the ordering system is triggered to order more stock from the supplier. The idea is that at some point every product in the world will be tagged in this way so it can always be identified and traced. In 2003 Gillette ordered 500 million RFID tags from manufacturers Alien Technology Corp to be added to its products.

As well as stock control, RFID technology is being used in an increasing number of applications. By the time you read this it could well have become a mainstream technology but at the time of writing it is still emerging. Recent (2005) applications include proximity card security systems in buildings, identification by a microchip inserted under the skin of domestic pets, and even tags used on nightclubbers. Pilot projects have been taking place to put RFID tags into vehicle licence plates, bank notes and hospital patients. A school in the US has already started to use RFID tags to monitor the movement of pupils. Not surprisingly some of these applications have raised concerns about the implications of this technology for individual privacy.

There are concerns that RFID could be used to tell,

> ... anyone who has the right kind of scanning device – from burglars to the government – what you have bought, where from, how much it cost, and anything else that might be added to an item's database entry, such as who bought it.

> (Shabi, 2003)

New manufacturing process

One of the reasons that a new device, like an RFID tag, has a chance of becoming mainstream technology is that a new manufacturing process has been invented that allows production on an industrial scale and at a relatively low cost.

Fluidic self-assembly (FSA) is a new manufacturing process that has been patented by Alien Technology Corp in the USA. In the FSA process tiny integrated circuits – trademarked as NanoBlocks – are suspended in liquid and flowed over a substrate surface that has correspondingly shaped 'holes' on it and into which the tiny circuits settle (Figure 47). The shape of the circuits and of the holes is arranged so that the circuits fall easily into place and are self-aligning. The NanoBlocks are then electrically connected to create the final integrated system. FSA allows tiny RFID circuits to be cost-effectively handled and packaged into electronic product code tags in huge volumes.

In addition to RFID tags this process is being used in the manufacture of flat-screen displays for use in high-definition television and computer screens. In addition to the advantages of reliability and high-speed volume manufacture (millions of NanoBlocks can be placed to within one micrometre of accuracy in minutes), the process can be used with a range of different surface materials and contours – for example permitting the manufacture of screen displays on flexible

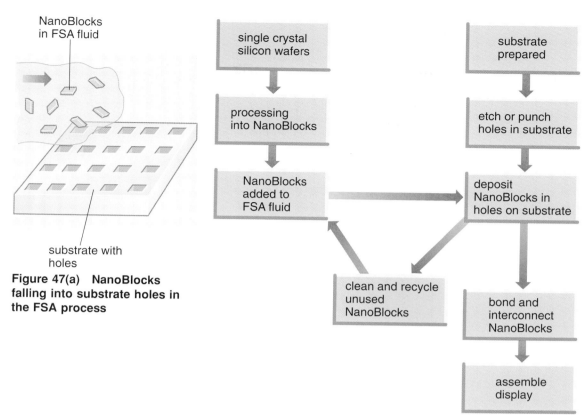

NanoBlocks
in FSA fluid

substrate with
holes

Figure 47(a)   NanoBlocks falling into substrate holes in the FSA process

Figure 47(b)   Fluidic self-assembly (FSA) process

plastic film (Figure 48). Section 5 looks in a little more detail at what can be achieved with nanotechnology.

Government policy, legislation and regulations

To a certain extent it's possible for governments to stimulate invention by providing incentives for manufacturers to develop new products and for consumers to buy and use them. One example of this process is in the field of vehicles powered by alternative fuels.

In the USA the Energy Policy Act of 1992 (EPAct) was passed to reduce US dependence on imported petroleum. The EPAct required federal and governmental departments with fleets over a certain size to acquire a percentage of alternative fuel vehicles (AFVs) capable of operating on non-petroleum fuels. Eligible alternative fuel vehicles included electric, hybrid-electric, liquefied natural gas, compressed natural gas (CNG), liquefied petroleum gas (LPG), hydrogen, fuel cell, and methanol. Biodiesel vehicles were added to this list in 2003.

Subsequent acts introduced and then extended tax credits on the purchase price of such vehicles, on the tax paid on the cost of installing alternative fuelling stations and on the cost of each gallon-equivalent sold. Furthermore acts like the Alternative Fuel Vehicle Acceleration Act of 2001 established a grant programme to fund demonstrations of AFVs and their commercial applications. Like the EPAct the funds were directed at federal and governmental departments with the intention they work in collaboration with manufacturers to encourage further development of this technology.

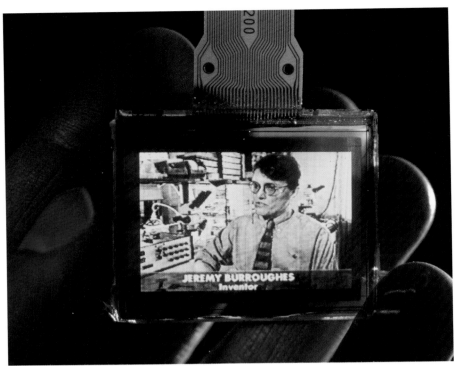

Figure 48 Screen developed by Cambridge Display Technology based on its ground-breaking development of light-emitting polymers (LEPs), which allow TV or computer displays to be created on flexible plastic sheet Source: Science Photo Library

Figure 49 Ford E-450 Cutaway school bus, powered by LPG Source: Ford Motor Company Limited

There are a number of visible outcomes of such schemes. Some conventional vehicles have been adapted by manufacturers to run on alternative fuels – in the US there are now many school buses powered by alternative fuels (Figure 49).

Automobile manufacturers are increasingly researching and prototyping alternative fuel vehicles in anticipation of the introduction of tighter antipollution regulations. One of a range of such projects is the race to offer fuel-cell technology, used for decades in spacecraft. Like batteries, fuel cells make electricity from chemical reactions. If hydrogen is the fuel, the waste products are simply water and heat. In 2003 DaimlerChrysler started supplying fuel-cell-powered buses to a number of European cities (Figure 50). Its website announced:

> With the current generation of Mercedes-Benz Citaro city buses, fuel-cell technology is now leaving the research stage and taking a crucial step ahead in the direction of economic efficiency and serviceability.

(DaimlerChrysler, 2003)

In my terms, the company had moved from invention to innovation.

Other than the examples given, can you think of inventions that resulted from a desire to help others?

Many inventions that help people with disabilities fall into this category.

Other than the examples given, can you think of inventions that took the opportunity offered by a new material, technology or manufacturing process?

New types of soft plastic composites enabled the development of the disposable contact lens.

Figure 50 Mercedes-Benz Citaro city bus starting trials in London in 2004 to test how well fuel-cell technology performs in an urban setting. The buses have no local emissions and their fuel, hydrogen, will be produced largely from renewable energy sources in the longer term. Source: EvoBus (UK) Ltd

Other than the examples given, can you think of inventions that came about because of government policy, legislation or regulations?

New building regulations introduced in 2002 required that all replacement windows had to have a minimum specified energy efficiency (U-value). This stimulated invention in glazing design.

2.2 How the process of invention works

I've looked at what motivates people and organisations to invent. I'll look more closely now at what's actually involved in inventing something.

2.2.1 Five steps to invention

Wherever invention occurs, whether with a lone inventor or in a creative team within an organisation, there seem to be common factors involved. There have been many attempts over the past 100 years to explain the creative process that occurs while people are attempting to solve problems. I'm going to combine ideas from two such models of the steps involved in creative problem solving or invention. The first source is from the economic historian Abbott P. Usher's book *A History of Mechanical Inventions* (1954) and the second is from Brian Lawson's book *How Designers Think* (1990). Combining the models of Usher and Lawson produces five key steps.

Step 1 – identification of the problem

Recognising an unsolved problem or one with an unsatisfactory current solution and determining to solve it.

Step 2 – exploration

Collecting information to help understand the problem better and produce initial solutions.

Step 3 – incubation

Periods of relaxation allow subconscious thought.

Step 4 – act of insight

A solution suddenly appears by a mental act that goes beyond the act of skill normally expected of a trained professional in that field.

Step 5 – critical revision

The solution is fully explored, tested and revised into a workable solution, possibly involving further acts of insight.

I will examine these key steps a little further. I've already covered the first two stages to some extent in looking at where inventions come from. Therefore I'll only deal briefly with steps 1 and 2 and look in more detail at the others.

2.2.2 Step 1 – identification of the problem

The activity of identifying a problem to be solved or a need to be met is a key step for the start of the innovation process. As you saw above there's a range of possible starting points. You've already seen examples where curiosity drives people to look for applications of certain scientific or technical principles such as Cockerell and air-cushion transport. Sometimes people identify an unsolved need, such as Percy Shaw and unlit roads. Sometimes people identify a need with an unsatisfactory current solution, such as James Dyson and his dissatisfaction with conventional wheelbarrows.

Another such starting point for invention is identifying possible new uses for existing products or processes. In such cases a key first step is the imagination to appreciate the technological possibilities and the market opportunities. Nowadays many organisations spend time actively seeking out new uses to which existing products and processes might be put as well as problems that need to be solved with new inventions. As you'll see in Section 4, in the case of the Post-it note the challenge for the 3M company was to find a use for a new type of adhesive – a glue that wasn't very sticky. In this case the 'problem' was one of an existing product in search of a market need rather than an established need requiring a new technological solution.

2.2.3 Step 2 – exploration

This is the period when, following the identification of the problem, attempts are made to understand it better and to make a stab at designing a solution. This might be a short process or it could take years and involve a detailed search for information, experimenting with different designs, even redefining the problem as a result of this activity.

Alexander Graham Bell adopted a problem-focused strategy when exploring the problem of designing a working telephone. This strategy is one typically used by scientists and engineers and involves exploring and redefining the problem exhaustively before coming up with a solution. A different approach, often adopted by designers, is to move quickly towards an outline solution based on their own experiences and preferences, which is then tested against the problem and modified as necessary to solve the problem more effectively. This more directed approach, known as a solution-focused strategy, was often used by Thomas Edison.

In the case of Edison's incandescent electric light discussed above this process of exploration took more than 12 months. Before he finally achieved his first working prototype Edison systematically experimented with thousands of different materials that might be used for a filament. His first patent was for a bulb with a platinum filament that, although it worked, was a complicated construction compared with the bulbs that were in mass production less than 2 years later. These used a carbonised bamboo filament, itself later replaced by other materials (Figure 51). The point is that this experimentation led to a better understanding of the problem and its possible solution, which resulted in the eventual design being more reliable.

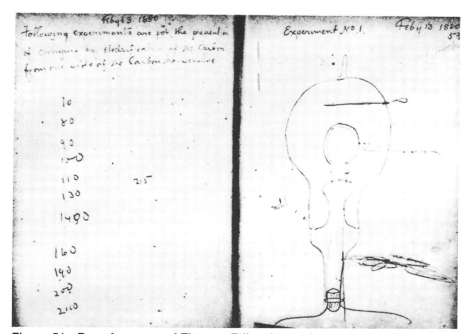

Figure 51   Page from one of Thomas Edison's notebooks showing the results of experiments on a carbonised filament electric lamp Source: Edison National Historic Site

2.2.4 Step 3 – incubation

Incubation is a period when the inventor, having been working on the problem for some time during identification and exploration, is no longer giving it conscious attention. The problem and its solution have been put to one side, on purpose or not, but the subconscious mind is capable of holding on to the problem. During this time, according to Roy (Open University, 2004, p. 34), 'the relaxed brain [is] repatterning information absorbed during the period of preparation often after receiving a new piece of information that is perceived as relevant'. I think what Roy means about repatterning is that the brain can make links between information – a new piece of information can cause a new link to be made and a new insight achieved. Although it's not often possible to demonstrate incubation taking place, there are numerous examples of inventors doing something unrelated to their invention when a breakthrough insight is triggered.

2.2.5 Step 4 – act of insight

Suddenly an insight suggests a solution, or the means of achieving a solution, to the inventor. Legendary examples include Newton observing an apple falling from a tree and having his insight into the laws of gravitation or Archimedes leaping from his bath and running naked through the streets shouting 'Eureka!' (I've found it). These vivid images point to the fact that creative ideas can occur when someone is not consciously trying to solve a problem.

These acts of insight are not only dependent upon the state of mind of the inventor, however, but also on the circumstances in which they occur. The image of Archimedes' moment of insight is familiar. Archimedes realised, allegedly as he lowered himself into his bath, that there was a relationship between his weight and the volume of water displaced.

Archimedes became excited because he realised this could provide him with a solution to a problem set for him by Hiero II, the ruler of Syracuse on the island of Sicily. Hiero had had a new crown made but suspected that his metal workers had stolen some of the gold and substituted it with a gold-silver alloy; so he wanted to know if the crown was pure gold or partly silver. Archimedes, a Syracusian mathematician and specialist in applied mechanics, realised that if the crown was partly silver it would be less dense than pure gold, would be bulkier for its weight and therefore would displace more water when immersed. As a consequence he had discovered a principle that would help him to determine whether the king's crown was pure gold or a mixture of gold and silver.

In his book *The Act of Creation* Arthur Koestler (1989) points out that at the critical moment Archimedes was able to make the connection between two previously unconnected trains of thought that his mind was processing (incubating) simultaneously. Nobody before Archimedes had brought together those separate ideas and if those particular circumstances had not pertained – thinking about the crown problem while taking a bath – that particular eureka moment would not have occurred. It might have occurred to someone else on another occasion because the history of invention shows that many minds are often working on the same problem (remember Edison and Swan on the electric light), but it is possible that many such moments have passed unnoticed for want of the necessary conjunction of inventive mind and propitious circumstances.

Koestler comments that rather than the mental achievement being to draw that particular conclusion, the achievement was actually in bringing together the two apparently unconnected ideas – a process he calls bisociation. Bisociation is one example of what is called associative thinking, which can lead to inventive solutions to problems. There are other ways of bringing together associations of ideas, knowledge and techniques from different areas: adaptation, transfer, combination, and analogy.

Adaptation

Adaptation is where a solution to a problem in one field is found by adapting an existing solution or a technical principle from another. For example Karl Dahlman adapted the hovercraft principle embodied in land and sea vehicles for use in the first hover lawn mower, the Flymo, in 1963 (Figure 52). In 2001 the car manufacturer Renault introduced the first mass-produced keyless vehicle (Figure 53). It had adapted smart card technology used in credit cards for use in vehicle security. The first generation version had lock and unlock buttons and was inserted into a slot in the dashboard to authorise starting the engine. For the second generation of these cards, introduced in 2003, the vehicle used proximity sensors to detect the presence of the card on the owner's person and unlocked the car once the user touched the door handle. When inside the car proximity sensors meant the driver only needed to press the starter button to start the engine.

Figure 52   Karl Dahlman pictured with his invention, the Flymo, which made use of the hover principle, 1963 Source: Flymo Ltd

Transfer

Transfer is where a technology, manufacturing process or material is transferred to another field to provide the basis for an invention. Earlier we saw how laser technology, originally thought to have few practical uses, was transferred to a variety of different applications including surgery, welding and cutting metal, bar-code readers, and audio CDs.

Combination

Combination is where two or more existing devices are combined to produce something new. For example the Toggle (Figure 54) combines a screwdriver and wire stripper for the outer and inner cores of an electric cable. It was designed by a student of an earlier

Figure 53   Renault's hands-free key card – an example of a solution adapted from another field Source: Renault (UK) Limited

(a)

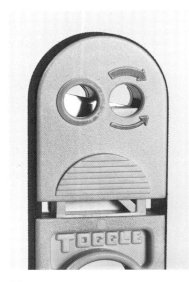

(b)

Figure 54   The Toggle combines a screwdriver and wire stripper in one tool. (a) The screwdriver can be angled. (b) Two holes with a blade for stripping thick and thin insulation from cables.

version of this course to combine into one the tools needed to wire an electric plug.

Analogy

Analogy draws on similar situations to provide ideas for invention and design. Alexander Graham Bell used the analogy of the human ear when designing telephone apparatus to receive sound. As mentioned above, his first receivers were much better than his transmitters where the analogy with the ear didn't work as well. When devising their flying machine, the Wright brothers used the analogy of soaring birds twisting their wings to restore balance. They designed the wings of their aircraft to be able to warp to achieve the same effect.

The moment of realisation of the answer to a problem, the flash of inventive insight portrayed by the eureka moment, is an important component of the inventive process. Without it there would be no significant improvements to existing technology or its products. But Usher believed that such acts of insight are as important to minor incremental inventions as they are to major radical inventions. And it's worth noting that insight doesn't always occur as a flash; sometimes it's a steady and growing awareness of the solution to a problem.

Chance

Another important source of inventions and scientific discoveries is chance, which is strongly associated with acts of insight. As well as the sort of painstaking work that either precedes an invention or goes into the steady improvement in performance, in the development of most inventions there's a moment when chance plays a part. Often people are looking for one thing but find another – perhaps working on one technology when they stumble on the principles behind another. The skill of the inventor lies initially in recognising the significance of a chance discovery and later of persuading others of its significance.

Chance played a part when the Swiss engineer George de Mestral conceived the idea for Velcro in 1948. After returning from a walk he found seed pods sticking to his socks and to his dog. When he examined the pods under a microscope he saw how tiny hooks had caught in the loops of the wool (Figure 55). He developed a method of reproducing the hooks and loops in woven nylon for use in clothing instead of buttons and zips (Figure 56). He called the product Velcro from a combination of velours (velvet) and crochet (hook) and the product went on to have many other uses including medicine (for joining the chambers of an artificial heart) and the space programme (for securing objects in a weightless environment).

Figure 55 Seed heads of this Goosegrass fruit are covered with prickly hooked bracts (modified leaves). They stick to the fur of passing animals and are carried away to colonise new territories. Source: Science Photo Library

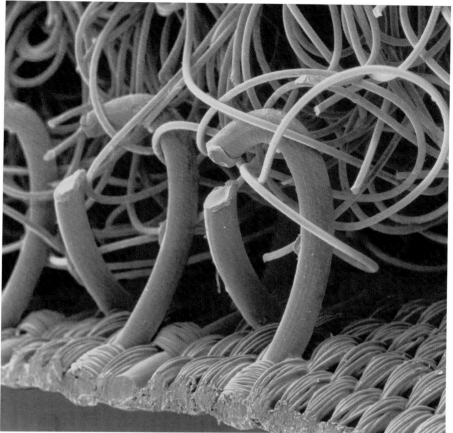

Figure 56 This electron-microscope picture of Velcro shows how closely the fastener copies the Goosegrass fruit Source: Science Photo Library

The tiny nylon hooks on one piece of Velcro catch the loops on the facing piece like seed burrs catch onto fur or wool. A thumbnail-size piece of Velcro contains about 750 hooks, with 12 500 loops on the other side. They can be fastened and unfastened thousands of times without wearing out.

Box 6 Chance and the invention of the microwave cooker

In 1945 Percy Spencer was an engineer working for Raytheon, a company that produced magnetrons, a key component of radar. One day he discovered that a chocolate and peanut bar in his pocket had melted. He realised that it must have been the high-frequency radio emissions from a magnetron that had heated the bar. Spencer then experimented by placing a bag of popcorn close to the magnetron – the popcorn exploded. Subsequent experiments showed that microwaves agitated the water molecules in food and cooked from the inside out, the opposite of conventional cooking.

The 1945 patent shows the original plan to have the food on a conveyor belt passing the cooker, with the speed of the belt controlling the cooking time (Figure 57). This idea didn't last long. Although it was a small company specialising in military electronics, Raytheon made the first commercial microwave cookers (Radarange) in 1947 (Figure 58). They were six feet high and cost the modern equivalent of around £40 000, so unsurprisingly sales were slow at first and were mainly to institutional catering units. It wasn't until the late 1960s, following a takeover, that a domestic worktop model was produced and sales began to pick up.

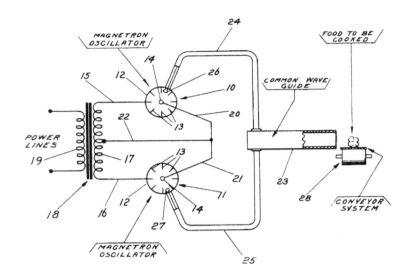

Jan. 24, 1950   P. L. SPENCER   2,495,429

METHOD OF TREATING FOODSTUFFS

Filed Oct. 8, 1945

INVENTOR.

PERCY L. SPENCER,

BY ...... ATTY.

Figure 57   Microwave cooker drawing from the 1945 patent Source: van Dulken, 2002

Figure 58 An early microwave cooker next to five modern cookers
Source: Raytheon Company

While chance observation can play a key part in achieving major progress, chance alone is not enough. Invention still requires the presence of an imaginative mind sensitised to the features of particular technological problems and busy thinking about solutions in order to capitalise on the chance occurrences. As Louis Pasteur put it, 'Where observation is concerned, chance favours only the prepared mind'.

Most aspects of invention (including steps 1 and 2 above and 5 below) can be, and usually are, influenced by economic incentives. Acts of insight, however, are bound up with the inventor's character, motivations, thinking style and thought processes – in other words, their individual creativity. No matter what the economic incentive for coming up with an invention, an individual will not be able to achieve the necessary act of insight without possessing the appropriate inventive skills, or acquiring them through training or practice. How often have you come across an inventive new product and thought, that seems obvious why didn't I think of that? But it takes a special skill to be the first person to make an unlikely connection and to come up with a creative solution to a problem.

Acts of insight might come more readily to people already working with a technology, but because such acts go beyond the skill expected of professionals it is sometimes possible for relative outsiders to come up with important inventions. For example Laszlo Biro was a journalist when he invented the ballpoint pen, John Boyd Dunlop was a veterinary surgeon when he invented the pneumatic tyre, and so on. So it is sometimes possible for *users* of technology to come up with improvements or replacements to existing technology when those already in the field see no need for change. However such acts of insight seldom lead to a fully formed invention.

2.2.6 Step 5 – Critical revision

Once a solution has been obtained it is then necessary to explore the extent to which it effectively solves the problem and where necessary revise it. Although more attention has been given to the moment of inspiration during the act of insight than to any other stage of invention, it is this process of *critical revision* that is usually the longest, most difficult and costly stage.

Genius is 1 per cent inspiration and 99 per cent perspiration.

(Thomas Edison, quoted in a newspaper interview)

As is implied by Thomas Edison's famous saying the insight needs to be coupled with hard work on the details to enable a bright idea to be transformed into a working prototype (Figure 59).

Figure 59   Edison in his laboratory in Orange, New Jersey, at 5.30 am on 16 June 1888 after having worked continuously for several days improving his phonograph Source: Edison National Historic Site

Like the process of exploration this critical revision might take months, as with Edison's light, or years. There were 4 years between James Watt's idea for improving the performance of Newcomen's steam engine by using a separate condenser to keep the cylinder as hot as possible, and his incorporation of this idea in the first full-size engine in 1769. Watt didn't have enough capital to devote his efforts full-time to solving the many technical problems involved in turning his idea into an efficient working machine. In addition he saw some of his ideas stolen and exploited by others. In a moment of despair that is familiar to inventors frustrated by the many obstacles in their path he wrote, 'Of all things in life there is nothing more foolish than inventing' (letter to his friend Dr Black, 1769).

Not only is the critical revision step necessary to move from the act of insight to a working invention, it is also a key factor in the process of transforming the invention into a commercially viable innovation. Indeed it was another 6 years before the first Watt steam engine went into commercial use for draining a Midlands coal mine in 1775, 10 years in all after his first act of insight. He was only able to achieve innovation thanks to his partnership with Birmingham manufacturer Matthew Boulton, which provided the capital and the entrepreneurial skills that Watt lacked but that were needed to help develop and sell his invention.

> The average British person uses 160 litres of water a day, and often in a wasteful way. What do you *identify* as the problem, and what *exploration* might you do next with a view to reducing the water used?

The problem is water shortages and increasing costs of supplying and buying water. At the consumer's end of this problem I would examine how water is used to see if any solutions suggest themselves. First thoughts include putting a brick in the cistern, using proximity-sensitive taps, and finding ways to store and use rainwater.

With practically any example of invention it's possible to see how it moves through these five stages as it is developed. As well as these stages common to inventions it's also possible to identify certain characteristics common to inventors.

2.2.7 Characteristics of inventors

In their classic book *The Sources of Invention* (1969) John Jewkes, David Sawers and Richard Stillerman observe the following about inventors, whether working outside or inside an organisation.

- Inventors tend to be absorbed with their own ideas and to feel strongly about their importance and potential.

- Inventors can be impatient with those who don't share their optimism.

- Inventors are often isolated because they are engrossed with ideas that imply change and that are resisted by others.

- Inventors can be right when others are eventually proved wrong. Accordingly inventors can appear eccentric because they have a minority view that challenges existing ideas.

- Inventors are often devoid of worldly knowledge, and in particular business knowledge, and therefore need special help in this aspect of innovation.

Some of these characteristics are useful to inventors during the process of invention. The ability to focus on a problem to the exclusion of everything else, the single-mindedness and determination to produce a solution, and the optimism that the solution is viable – all of these can help the inventor overcome the many obstacles to invention.

However some of these very characteristics can become liabilities when applied to the process of innovation. This requires the skills of working with others in a team – the ability to persuade others of the worth of the invention; the patience to accept criticism; the flexibility to compromise and change the design if required, say, by the manufacturing process; the open-mindedness to accept input from others with more expertise in a particular aspect of innovation, such as marketing.

2.3 Technology push and market pull

So far you've seen that there are two general drivers of invention. One is the scientific and technological knowledge and skills that can be applied to invent a new product or process. The other is the recognition of a need or a potential market for an invention. But is one more important than the other? I'll consider briefly two simple models that explain how the innovation process starts.

2.3.1 Technology push

The technology push model is a simple linear model that suggests that the innovation process starts with an idea or a discovery – it is sometimes called idea push (Figure 60). Sometimes this is by a creative individual who has the knowledge and imagination to realise its significance and the practical skills to transform the idea or discovery into an invention. An example from earlier is Cockerell and his hovercraft. You also saw, with the invention of the laser, that inventors don't always foresee the ultimate commercial applications of their invention. However more often nowadays the starting point is basic scientific research or applied research and development (R&D) in organisations. This proceeds through design and development into a product that can be manufactured effectively and economically and then sold on the market.

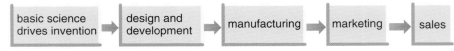

Figure 60   Technology push model

The market is seen as a receptacle for the output of scientific research and invention; therefore an increase in basic and applied R&D should lead to an increase in innovation. In the past government support for innovation in many countries consisted of bolstering science and the R&D supply aspect.

In his book *Enabling Innovation* Boru Douthwaite (2002) criticised this process and dubbed it the 'over-the-wall model'. An R&D team assumes it knows enough about the users' needs to develop a new product without involving them in its specification or design. The team simply develops the product and tosses it 'over the wall' to users in the belief that there's a need for it, the technology is complete and ready to use, and users are technically skilled enough to use it without help.

Now there are times when this approach can work. For example Sony's development of the Walkman personal stereo cassette player was not in response to any need identified by market research (Figure 61). One of the cofounders of the company was using a Sony portable stereo tape recorder and standard-size headphones to listen to a cassette. He complained about the weight of this system to the president Akio Morita. Morita ordered his engineers to remove the recording circuit from one of their small cassette recorders (the Pressman) and replace it with a stereo amplifier. In addition he asked for lightweight headphones to be developed. The headphones turned out to be the biggest technical challenge in the project and were the most innovative component – everything else was a new application of existing technology.

Figure 61   Example of successful technology push, the first Sony Walkman
Source: Sony UK Ltd

Proposed in 1979 and manufactured from 1980, Sony was first to market with this innovative product

There was scepticism within the firm as to the market appeal of a cassette player without a recording facility but Morita – acting as a product champion – pushed through the idea. Almost from its launch the Walkman was successful. As with many innovative products no amount of market research would have identified a specific need because one did not exist. Success came from encouraging a latent need by providing people with an innovative product they hadn't known they wanted.

But such instincts on the part of a manufacturer as to what might make for a successful product are not always right. For example Morita had assumed it was less antisocial to include a second headphone socket so that two people could share their listening experience. He had also included a button-activated microphone so that the two listeners could talk to each other over the music on a 'hot line'. When this idea didn't catch on and it became clear that the early users really valued this product as a personal device, those extra features were removed.

But though the technology push model might describe the innovation process for some products, it only tells part of the story. There are numerous examples of inventions that are good ideas, scientifically or technologically sound and available to the market, yet fail to become successful innovations. The notion that if an idea is good enough technology push will help it to overcome all obstacles to its innovation, is a romantic one, but unrealistic.

Box 7 Technology push doesn't always work – the Dvorak keyboard

The QWERTY keyboard layout was developed by Christopher Latham Sholes to slow down the typist (Figure 62). The mechanical typewriters of the time often jammed if two adjoining keys were struck rapidly in succession. Sholes rearranged the keys so that the most commonly used letter sequences were spread out, slower to find and would converge from opposite sides of the machine. When typewriter mechanisms became more efficient the original justification for the QWERTY arrangement disappeared.

Figure 62 Prototype of the QWERTY typewriter patented by Christopher Latham Sholes in 1868 that formed the basis of the first commercial typewriter, the Remington No.1 in 1874 Source: Smithsonian Institute

At this point in its development a few of the characters have yet to find their final location – this prototype starts 'QWE.TY'

In 1932 Professor August Dvorak of the University of Washington used time-and-motion studies to create a more efficient keyboard layout (Figure 63). The most frequently used letters in English – A, O, E, U, I, D, H, T, N, S – were placed on the central, home row that could then account for around 70 per cent of the typing, compared with 32 per cent of the QWERTY keyboard's home keys. Dvorak also altered the balance of keys controlled by the normally weaker left-hand from 57 per cent with the QWERTY layout to 44 per cent.

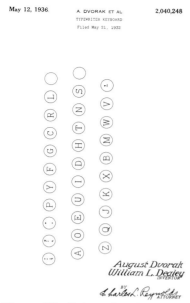

May 12, 1936.   A. DVORAK ET AL   2,040,248
                     TYPEWRITER KEYBOARD
                     Filed May 21, 1932

Figure 63 Patent drawing of Dvorak's improved non-QWERTY keyboard layout
Source: US Patent 2040248

However by this time there was significant vested interest in keeping the dominant design, both for manufacturers and users trained on the QWERTY layout. Dvorak's keyboard was not taken up and the QWERTY standard still dominates the market. This makes a nonsense of the saying attributed to Ralph Waldo Emerson that,

> If a man ... make a better mouse trap than his neighbor, though he build his house in the woods, the world will make a beaten path to his door.

So if the market can be resistant to good new technology what role does the market play in encouraging invention?

2.3.2 Market pull

The alternative market pull model suggests that the stimulus for innovation comes from the needs of society or a particular section of the market (Figure 64). These might be needs perceived by an entrepreneur or manufacturer like Shaw and his cat's-eyes or they might be clearly articulated by consumers. According to this model a successful approach to innovation would be to research the market thoroughly first, assess what needs exist, how far they are met by existing products and processes and how the needs might be met more effectively by means of a new or improved innovation. The theory then is that once the appropriate technology is developed a receptive market is assured because the innovation process has been tailored to meet a definite need.

Figure 64 Market pull model

Therefore this model adds a stage of exploring market need before the invention stage of the technology push model. This approach might be characterised by the classic saying, 'necessity is the mother of invention'.

Douthwaite identifies two levels of exploring market need. The first level he calls the consultancy model. In this the R&D team consults users about needs but doesn't involve them in the development process because it thinks its own experience and its ability to ask users the right questions will provide all the information it needs. Douthwaite thinks this process might work for upgrading existing technologies but is poor for developing novel products and systems. For that he suggests the best approach is the codevelopment model.

He suggests more radical inventions require an R&D team to codevelop the product or technology in conjunction with potential users. For instance work done by consumer electronics company Philips in researching users' needs has involved users in the testing of products at various stages. At the preconcept design stage the user may be asked what sort of products do they want. At the prototype stage the user may be asked how well does this prototype work and does it meet their needs. At the post-purchase stage the user may be asked what incremental improvements to this existing product would they like to see. Even when a product is reaching maturity the user is asked what, if anything, would they like to see taking its place.

Critics of the market pull explanation point out that because an important need exists it is no guarantee that an invention will emerge to meet that need. There are many examples of long-standing needs that have yet to be satisfactorily met despite the efforts of many inventive minds, such as cures for many medical conditions, and safe road transport. Moreover the notion of a coherent market with a clearly identifiable set of needs is simplistic (Figure 65). In reality there is a complex range of sectors within the market for a particular product type. A very familiar example is the car market, with separate sectors for the supermini, family saloons and estates, people carriers, executive cars, sports cars, four-wheel-drive cars, and so on. Some theorists argue that over-concentration on the marketing concept has led companies to become preoccupied with incremental and often trivial innovations at the expense of radical breakthroughs, which are more likely to be achieved through technology push.

Figure 65   Motorcycle airbag in a crash test. Another example of market pull? Not entirely, many motorcyclists are resistant so most motorcycle manufacturers have not seen the need for R&D. Source: Science Photo Library

It is true that fulfilling human needs is an important incentive for inventors and innovators. This is especially so for improvements to existing products and innovations aimed at obvious needs, such as safety (car airbags), health (new medicines), productivity (process innovations), food supply (new strains of wheat and rice). So there is some truth in the view that necessity is the mother of invention; but this is only part of the story. Consumers cannot demand products that have not yet been conceived but needs can be created by the emergence of an innovation.

A search for the origins of the gasoline-powered motorcar reveals that it was not necessity that inspired its inventors to complete their task. The automobile was not developed in response to some grave international horse crisis or horse shortage. National leaders, influential thinkers, and editorial writers were not calling for the replacement of the horse, nor were ordinary citizens anxiously hoping that some inventors would soon fill a serious societal and personal need for motor transportation. In fact, during the first decade of existence, 1895–1905, the automobile was a toy, a plaything for those who could afford to buy one.

(Basalla, 1988, p. 198)

Remember the label 'toy' was also applied to early versions of Bell's telephone and Berliner's gramophone.

Indeed the need for motor vehicles arose after, not before, their invention. This invention opened up possibilities for transportation that had not previously existed and stimulated a desire to share in the benefits that were offered when it became an innovation (Figure 66). And the very existence of a new innovation can create previously non-existent needs leading to new inventions. It might just as easily be said that, 'invention is the mother of necessity', in this and in many other cases of new technological products.

Figure 66 Karl Benz's pioneering three-wheeled car of 1888 Source: Science Photo Library

Designed by German engineer Karl Benz, this car was one of the first in the world to be put into production (not a one-off). It was of similar type to Benz's first car of 1885 but with an improved design. This four-seat vehicle with three wooden wheels was powered by a single-cylinder 1.69 litre four-stroke Benz industrial engine placed horizontally over the rear axle.

2.3.3 Coupling model

There are examples where either technology or the market appears to be more significant in stimulating invention but the majority of innovations involve a creative coupling of technological and market factors. In some respects successful innovation is a case of the survival of the fittest. Failure can come both from not getting the technology right and from misjudging the market. Success is more likely if the focus is not too one-dimensional but rather a balance between technology and market considerations.

But a key challenge with invention and innovation is that both technology and the market are changing constantly. What is technically unachievable today may be possible in a few years time due to scientific advances, sometimes in an unrelated field. Likewise what cannot be sold today may come to be regarded as a necessity by future consumers.

The relationships between advancing science and technology and a changing market are complex. The skill of the companies and the people operating at the interfaces between these areas is to make the connection between technological and market possibilities. It can be a creative process similar to the associative thinking involved in the original invention itself, and is often the province of the entrepreneur.

This coupling between technology and market needs is important at every stage of the innovation process, from the first flash of inspiration, through the entire research, design and development work to the introduction of the new product or process onto the market.

Although the innovation process clearly contains both technology and market elements, any model of the process has to introduce some sense of interaction and growing complexity. It must have feedback loops and a variety of links both between science, technology and the market place, and between innovating firms and the outside world. Rothwell's coupling model starts to suggest this complexity (Figure 67).

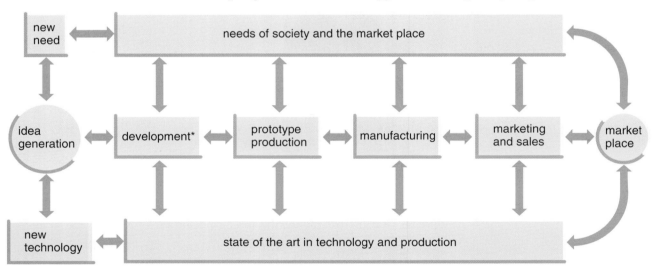

Figure 67   Roy Rothwell's coupling model of innovation (*in later papers amended to 'research, design and development') Source: adapted from Rothwell, 1992

Do you have a personal example of market pull *not* generating a product – in other words do you need a product that doesn't exist, or a better product than the one that does exist?

2.4   Preparing for innovation

Many inventors have said that having the idea for an invention is the easy part. This is often demonstrated by the frequency of examples of simultaneous invention. At one exhibition of inventions I attended there were three separate portable ladders to escape from fires, two systems for using rainwater to flush toilets, two types of portable vehicle wheel clamp, and two methods of reducing red-eye in flash photography. In most cases of technological innovation only one of the competing technologies goes on to achieve significant success. The challenge lies in the development of an inventive idea into a successful design and innovation – to complete the difficult journey from idea to market.

Once inventors seek to move beyond the stage of the prototype that demonstrates the feasibility of their invention they move into another territory. Manufacturing an invention on a large scale can involve a different set of problems from those involved in devising an invention and producing a prototype.

The prototype might not be sufficiently attractive to look at or easy to use to appeal to buyers. It might not be made of materials suitable for the manipulation required by a volume manufacturing process, or for the degree of safe and reliable performance required by a commercial innovation on sale to the public. Consequently development often involves the search for new materials or for new uses for existing materials, both of which can involve further invention. Further, existing technical methods might be inadequate for economic volume manufacture and a new machine or a new process might need to be invented.

Given the technical complexity and the level of investment required to manufacture most innovative products, it is necessary to be able to predict and control the manufacturing process precisely. Depending on the nature of the product, it may be that during the invention phase a mixture of empirical bench work and scientific investigation was used. Less technologically complex inventions are likely to have involved mostly an empirical, cut-and-try approach, with a scientific approach needed for more complex inventions. Either way when it comes to the precision required for large-scale manufacture there is an increasing need to understand how an invention works, or how a material behaves in a certain way under certain conditions, or how a particular manufacturing method is carried out, in order to be able to control the overall process. For this level of understanding a scientific input is usually invaluable, although craft skill and empirical know-how remain important even for leading-edge innovations.

Finally as well as the increasing precision of the manufacturing technology needed to progress from invention to innovation, development also calls for more careful consideration of the commercial aspects, market needs and sales potential – the likely costs of manufacture, size of market, sales price, selling strategy, profit margin, visual and functional design, and so on. These market considerations are examined in more detail later in the course.

SAQ 4

What are the four main factors that motivate individuals to invent?

SAQ 5

What are the four main factors that motivate organisations to invent?

SAQ 6

From the brief description of Carlson's invention of xerography given above, how do the five key steps of the Usher–Lawson model fit that particular example?

SAQ 7

To what extent would you describe the following inventions as predominantly arising from technology push or from market pull?

(a) early motor cars

(b) car airbags

(c) photocopier

(d) high-yielding varieties of wheat and rice

(e) laser.

Key points of Section 2

- Individuals are motivated to invent by one or more factors: curiosity; constructive discontent about a product; a desire to help others; a desire to make money.

- Organisations invent for a number of reasons: business strategy; the need to improve existing products and processes; new materials become available, as do technologies and manufacturing processes; government policy, legislation and regulations.

- The process of invention involves the stages of: identification, exploration, incubation, act of insight, critical revision.

- Inventive ideas often occur due to associative thinking, which brings together ideas, knowledge and techniques from different areas. Inventors also use adaptation, transfer, combination and analogy.

- Chance often plays a significant role in invention.

- Inventors often have the ability to focus on a problem to the exclusion of everything else, and are single-minded and determined, and have an optimism about finding a viable solution.

- Innovation requires teamwork, the ability to persuade others, the patience to accept criticism, the flexibility to compromise and the open-mindedness to accept input from others.

- The technology push model suggests the innovation process starts with an idea or a discovery. The market pull model suggests the stimulus for innovation comes from the needs of the market. The coupling model suggests interaction between innovators and the market.

- Having the idea for an invention is often easy compared with transforming it into a marketable innovation.

The key points for Section 2 meet learning outcomes 1.1, 1.3, 1.5, 1.6, 1.7, 1.14, 2.1, 2.2 and 4.1.

3 Innovation

As you've seen above, many inventors have discovered that innovation – getting their ideas made and sold – is harder than invention. To bring an invention to the market there are a number of obstacles to overcome – technical, financial and organisational. The invention has to be made using appropriate materials and manufacturing processes depending on the nature of the product and the numbers required. Then, once an innovation is available to potential buyers, there are a number of factors that influence how well it will sell and how rapidly it is likely to diffuse. Factors affecting sales and diffusion include characteristics of the innovation itself, conditions of the market and any relevant regulations.

Finally, although innovations generally offer progress, some complement existing ways of doing things and have a sustaining effect for a technology or an industry. Some innovations though are more disruptive and can lead to significant changes in society.

3.1 Overcoming obstacles to innovation

3.1.1 Getting the technology to work

A fundamental requirement for successful innovation is that the invention must work. It mustn't violate any scientific laws and it must be capable of being transformed into a working prototype. In addition to getting the technology to work it must be designed to be easy to use and reliable, attractive, safe and environmentally friendly. It must also be designed so it's capable of being manufactured on a scale that makes it economic to produce and to buy.

Sometimes an idea for an invention is ahead of the technology, materials, components or knowledge needed to deliver it. The idea for television was suggested in 1877, almost 50 years before its actual invention. While the basic principles that were to lead to television were understood by the scientific community, these hadn't yet been translated into the practical working components required – cathode ray tubes for example. Furthermore even the idea needed further time to develop. At first it was perceived as a two-way interactive device for talking to others on screen – the 'telephonoscope' (Figure 68). Then it was imagined as the transfer over distance of a single image onto paper ('telephotography') or screen ('electric telescope'). Eventually the idea of transmitting moving images gained ground but it was still being thought of as a means of two-way communication (an extension of the telephone) until the first regular one-way television transmissions started in London in 1932.

Sometimes the early prototypes of an invention just don't work well. As mentioned in Section 1, Thomas Edison invented the phonograph in 1877 (Figure 69). A diaphragm transformed sound into vibrations in an attached needle, which in turn traced a pattern on tinfoil stretched around a hand-cranked drum. When the process was reversed the pattern recreated the sound, which returned through the diaphragm.

EDISON'S TELEPHONOSCOPE (TRANSMITS LIGHT AS WELL AS SOUND).

(Every evening, before going to bed, Pater- and Materfamilias set up an electric camera-obscura over their bedroom mantel-piece, and gladden their eyes with the sight of their Children at the Antipodes, and converse gaily with them through the wire.)

Paterfamilias (in Wilton Place). " BEATRICE, COME CLOSER, I WANT TO WHISPER."   *Beatrice (from Ceylon).* " YES, PAPA DEAR."
Paterfamilias. " WHO IS THAT CHARMING YOUNG LADY PLAYING ON CHARLIE'S SIDE?"
Beatrice. " SHE'S JUST COME OVER FROM ENGLAND, PAPA.   I'LL INTRODUCE YOU TO HER AS SOON AS THE GAME'S OVER!"

Figure 68 '**Edison's Telephonoscope', Punch cartoon dated 9 December 1879** Source: Punch Cartoon Library

Figure 69   Edison's earliest model of the phonograph, 1877

While Edison's first 'talking machines' caused quite a stir for 6 months and led to considerable speculation as to their potential uses (Figure 70), it soon became clear the invention had been launched prematurely. Edison's list of possible uses for his invention was optimistic (see Box 8), particularly his preference that it should be used as a serious business machine. The tinfoil cylinders of the first phonographs played for little more than a minute and reproduced the human voice in a barely recognisable form.

It took almost 20 years of further development before a reliable phonograph started to become widely available for domestic use (Figure 71). Wax recording cylinders replaced the tinfoil, constant-speed electric motors (and later on, cheaper clockwork mechanisms) replaced Edison's initial hand crank, recording techniques and quality steadily improved (early recording artists had to record each cylinder individually), then by the early years of the twentieth century the recording disk had replaced the cylinder.

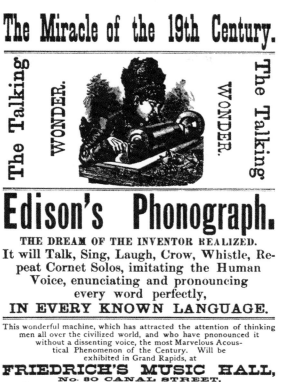

The Miracle of the 19th Century.

The Talking WONDER. WONDER. The Talking

Edison's Phonograph.

THE DREAM OF THE INVENTOR REALIZED.

It will Talk, Sing, Laugh, Crow, Whistle, Repeat Cornet Solos, imitating the Human Voice, enunciating and pronouncing every word perfectly,

IN EVERY KNOWN LANGUAGE.

This wonderful machine, which has attracted the attention of thinking men all over the civilized world, and who have pnonounced it without a dissenting voice, the most Marvelous Acoustical Phenomenon of the Century. Will be exhibited in Grand Rapids, at

FRIEDRICH'S MUSIC HALL,

NO. 80 CANAL STREET,

Commencing WEDNESDAY, JULY 3d,

Exhibited Daily July 3d. 4th 5th and 6th.

To accommodate those who desire not only to hear the Phonograph speak, but to inspect and examine it closely, it will be exhibited every day from 10 to 12 a. m., from 2 to 5 p. m., and from 8 to 10 evenings.   The operator will fully explain the machine and test its powers at every entertainment.
Special attention paid to Ladies and Children.

ADMISSION, only 25 Cents,   Children, 10 Cents.

Eagle Steam Job Rooms—W. C. Dennis & Co.

Figure 70   The poster announces 4 days of demonstrations of the phonograph in Grand Rapids, Michigan, during the summer of 1878 Source: Gelatt, 1977

The story of the unfinished state of the Edison phonograph could be repeated for many famous technological innovations:

Figure 71   Berliner gramophone, about 1891. Its turntable was rotated manually, to play 180 mm (7 inch) disks at a designed speed of 70 rpm. Source: Gelatt, 1977

- The cameras of the 1840s called for exposure times of 10 to 90 seconds.

- The cumbersome and slow typewriters of the mid-nineteenth century were scarcely an improvement over writing with a pen.

- The first commercial internal-combustion engine, the vertical Otto and Langen engine of 1866, stood 7-foot tall and delivered 3 horsepower.

- The Wright brothers' first powered airplane stayed aloft only 57 seconds.

- The television receivers of the 1920s displayed small images (1.5 by 2 inches) that were blurred and flickered badly (Figure 72).

- The first electronic computer occupied 1800 square feet of floor space and weighed 30 tons.

At first glance none of these appeared to be likely prospects for the basis of a new industry, yet all did so.

(Basalla, 1988, p. 142)

Figure 72 First television picture, 1925 Source: Science & Society Picture Library

John Logie Baird, inventor of a mechanically scanned television system, was able to transmit this blurred but recognisable human face. On 26 January 1926 he successfully demonstrated his invention to members of the Royal Institution, and *The Times* reported on the successful test of the 'Televisor'.

Box 8   Edison's ideas for uses of his phonograph

A year after inventing the phonograph Edison published an article listing ten ways in which the public might find the invention useful. In his personal order of priority these were:

1   letter writing and all kinds of dictation without the aid of a stenographer

2   phonographic books, which will speak to blind people without effort on their part

3   the teaching of elocution

4   reproduction of music

5   the 'family record' – a registry of sayings, reminiscences, and so on by members of a family in their own voices, and the last words of dying persons

6   music boxes and toys

7   clocks that should announce in articulate speech the time for going home or going to meals

8   the preservation of languages by exact reproduction of the manner of pronouncing

9   educational purposes, such as preserving the explanations made by a teacher, so that the pupil can refer to them at any moment, and spelling or other lessons placed upon the phonograph for convenience in committing to memory

10   connection with the telephone, so as to make that instrument an auxiliary in the transmission of permanent and invaluable records, instead of being the recipient of momentary and fleeting communication.

Music reproduction was ranked fourth because Edison thought this was a relatively trivial use of his invention. Even when he started production of phonographs on a commercial basis – after a 10-year diversion into developing and improving the electric light – he concentrated on selling it as a dictation machine, resisting efforts to market it for playing music. Other people saw and exploited the entertainment potential of Edison's invention and carried out improvements to the technology to make it an effective and attractive product. It was not until the mid 1890s, however, that the inventor himself came to accept that the primary use of this invention was for entertainment rather than as a useful piece of office equipment.

Sometimes the take-up of an invention is delayed by the non-availability of suitable materials to enable the invention to perform effectively or by the lack of development of a process technology to enable the efficient and cost-effective manufacture of the invention. For example Frank Whittle's turbojet engine patented in 1930 did not work efficiently until manufacturers developed a new nickel-chrome alloy to enable the turbine blades to withstand the high temperatures and stresses involved (Figures 73 and 74). And it could not be manufactured on an industrial scale until improvements had been made in metal processing and manufacture. This was not achieved on any significant scale until after the Second World War, more than 10 years after patenting. By this time Whittle had long since allowed his basic patent to lapse because his employers, the RAF, had little faith in the feasibility or potential of his invention in the early stages of its development.

Figure 73   First Whittle jet-propulsion flight engine, which ran in 1937 and flew in 1941
Source: Science & Society Picture Library

Figure 74   Frank Whittle and the W1 turbojet engine, pictured in 1988
Source: Science & Society Picture Library

Sometimes the obstacle is that the most appropriate application for a new technology hasn't yet been found. There are often a number of different uses to which any invention can be put. The first uses are not necessarily those for which an invention will eventually become known. The first steam engines were not for transportation but were used to pump water from mines. The most widespread application of the hovercraft principle is in hovering lawn mowers. Soft paper tissue was developed by Kimberley-Clark as a substitute for cotton wool as a medical dressing during the First World War. As a result of looking for new applications it was marketed as a make-up remover from 1924. It was only when users reported on its qualities for nose blowing that it was relaunched as Kleenex tissue handkerchief (Figure 75).

3.1.2   Getting finance and organisational backing

Like talk, ideas are cheap. Even generating a prototype of an invention can be cheap compared with the resources needed to produce and market an innovation. The independent inventor or designer is likely to have to rely on family and friends for financial backing, particularly in the early stages. Seed capital is sometimes available in the form of innovation grants from government bodies and departments to individuals and small businesses. Eventually, however, most inventors need to access the sort of funds only a company or a venture capitalist can provide.

Some inventors decide to go into business for themselves because they distrust organisations or because they failed to persuade an organisation to take up their invention. The inventor of the Workmate portable workbench, Ron Hickman, was one such inventor-entrepreneur. Hickman had developed craft skills through 10 years of practical experience as a designer with Lotus cars. As mentioned in Section 1 he was also a do-it-yourself enthusiast who became dissatisfied with existing devices after damaging a chair that was being used to support a piece of wood he was sawing.

New-type handkerchief

checks the spread of Colds!

use

KLEENEX

THE *Tissue* HANDKERCHIEF

In place of germ-carrying handkerchiefs

...no washing! no self-infection!

No more passing on your colds to the whole family now! For unhygienic germ-filled handkerchiefs are out—and Kleenex is in! Kleenex checks the spread of colds. You use each tissue once only and destroy it—germs and all! You don't keep reinfecting yourself either. Colds go quicker, and Kleenex avoids all possibility of raw red noses. You can use 30 Kleenex tissues for the average cost of laundering two handkerchiefs. Get the Kleenex habit today!

Women everywhere also find Kleenex invaluable for removing Cold Cream and to apply Cosmetics.

6ᴰ 1⁄ 2⁄3

At all Chemists and Stores. In handy pull-out boxes.

No Waste! Pull them out— the next pop up ready for use! Always tidy!

Figure 75   Originally used for medical dressings during the First World War, then for sanitary towels and then make-up removers, the use of paper tissue as a handkerchief took some time to evolve Source: John Frost Newspaper Service

He designed and built a prototype of a combined workbench and sawhorse. After he found it to be unexpectedly useful, he developed it further and by 1968 he had the mark 1 Workmate design (Figure 76). Next he tried to persuade relevant organisations in the DIY field of the commercial potential of his idea. However none of them was willing to risk investing in a completely new product for which there was no clear demand, being an unusual hybrid of sawhorse, vice and workbench. In 1968 Stanley Tools estimated potential sales could be measured in 'dozens rather than in hundreds' – by 1981 the 10 millionth Workmate had been sold.

Figure 76   Mark 1 Workmate manufactured by Ron Hickman, 1968
Source: Science & Society Picture Library

Hickman, however, had confidence in his invention and decided to manufacture the product himself. By 1972 he had sold 25 000 Workmate benches by mail order. Existing manufacturers of DIY products began to take an interest, including Black & Decker, which had been among the companies offered a licence in 1968. In 1972 Black & Decker finally took a licence on the Workmate. Even then the story was not straightforward.

It still required the efforts of a key individual within Black & Decker (Walter Goldsmith, general manager) to champion the product and persuade others that investing in the Workmate was an economically sound idea. He was helped in this by Hickman's success up to that point, which demonstrated the existence of a market for this unique product. Hickman would certainly not have been able to achieve sales of 10 million units over that period had he continued on his own. It was only by handing over control of his innovation to a large organisation for production and further product development that mass-market sales were achieved for the Workmate (Figures 77 and 78).

To be fair, potential investors often have to make judgements about whether to support an invention on the evidence of early prototypes. Perhaps it is not surprising there are many examples of companies that have turned down what became highly successful and profitable inventions. With hindsight it is easy to scoff at such apparent blunders but the decisions were often made for entirely sensible reasons. The invention might have been outside the company's existing product

Figure 77   Workmate 2, manufactured by Black & Decker Source: DIY Photo Library

Figure 78   Black & Decker's Wm675 Workmate, 2004 Source: © Copyright Black and Decker Inc, Workbench, 2004; reproduced with permission

range at a time when their existing products were selling well and profitably. Some organisations resist investing in 'outside' inventions but rather prefer to develop their own in-house ideas – this is known as the not-invented-here attitude. The production, marketing and commercialisation of an unproven new idea are likely to be costly and run the risk of failure.

It takes a certain amount of courage to decide that an invention does have potential, particularly on the evidence of a partially developed prototype. Sometimes it takes a small, new company with an informal organisational structure, entrepreneurial values and little to lose to risk bringing a new technology to the market place. I will say more on this when I deal with sustaining and disruptive innovations.

As writer Arthur C. Clarke said,

> Every revolutionary idea ... seems to evoke three stages of reaction. They may be summed up by the phrases:
>
> 1   It's completely impossible – don't waste my time.
>
> 2   It's possible, but it's not worth doing.
>
> 3   I said it was a good idea all along.

(Clarke, 1968)

3.1.3 Choosing appropriate materials and manufacturing process

The choice of materials and manufacturing process for a particular new product is an important aspect of the innovation process. It is not necessarily the case that the materials chosen for the early prototypes of an invention are those best suited for the larger-scale manufacture of the innovation. Choice of materials can affect the performance, quality and economic manufacture of most new products, so it's important to choose wisely.

While inventors and designers usually need to seek specialist assistance when it comes to choosing materials, it helps to inform their choices if they have a broad overview of the main types of material and their properties. Designers need to consider a range of materials properties:

● performance – behaviour of the material in the finished product

● processing – behaviour of the material during manufacture

● economic – cost and availability of material

● aesthetic – appearance and texture of processed material.

Increasingly *environmental impacts* are playing a part in the choice of materials. These impacts include the energy consumed and pollution produced in the extraction and preprocessing of raw materials as well as their final processing into a product; the effect of chosen materials on the life of the product; and the potential for recycling and environmentally sound disposal at the end of the product's life. With all these factors to consider it's not surprising the final choice of materials for a new product is often a compromise, strongly influenced by the costs both of the material itself and of processing it.

The T211 DVD provided with this course contains the CES materials and processes database, which you might find helpful when you come to work on your project.

In the same way that inventors and designers need knowledge of the range of materials available, they equally need to know the strengths and limitations of a range of manufacturing processes. As with the choice of suitable materials for a product there will often be a number of feasible processes. The following are the different criteria that can be applied to identify an optimum process in a particular case.

● Cost – the capital cost of new equipment, the cost of dedicated tools such as moulds, the labour costs of setting up and operating the process, and the assumed rate of depreciation for tools and equipment.

● Cycle time – how long it takes to process one item (part, component or product).

● Product quality – the standards required in terms of performance properties, surface finish and dimensional tolerances, and maintaining quality over time.

● Flexibility – how easy it is to produce different designs on the same equipment.

● Materials utilisation – the amount of waste material generated during processing.

The relative importance of these criteria will vary depending on the volume to be produced and on whether the products will be identical or the same equipment will be used to manufacture different designs.

The ability to design and make a new product to the optimum quality specifications at the lowest cost and in the shortest time has been the general goal of manufacturers since the start of the industrial revolution. The means by which this goal has been achieved have developed as materials, techniques and the organisation of production have evolved. Not only has the transformation of the manufacturing process enabled many inventions of increasing complexity to reach the market and become successful innovations, the manufacturing process itself has been the subject of much innovation.

In a number of the examples earlier in this block you've seen that the development of most innovations includes significant reductions in cost, which make the product affordable by larger numbers of customers. (Examples include the BIC ballpoint pen, Edison's electric light and the electronic tagging of products.) Often this cost breakthrough is due to decisions made in the area of materials and manufacture. A new material might be used in the product that makes it easier and cheaper to manufacture (the use of plastic for the bodies of ballpoint pens); a new assembly process might be more efficient with fewer components and fewer stages (recall that the assembly of Edison's electric light was reduced from 200 to 20 steps and the labour time from 1 hour to 20 seconds); a new manufacturing process might become applicable to the production of an innovation (fluidic self-assembly allowing production of RFID tags on an industrial scale).

Further savings might be achieved by regularly reviewing the design and manufacturing process for a product and aiming where possible for simplification and integration. Can the product be redesigned with fewer parts? Can parts be designed to serve more than one function? Can a new or different principle be used? Can parts be redesigned for ease of fabrication? Can fasteners be eliminated or reduced by using tabs or snap-fits? Can a product be designed to use standard components?

The basis of mass production is the complete interchangeability of components and the simplicity of attaching them to each other. With this increasing reliance on interchangeability in a world dependent on mass-produced products, it becomes more important than ever to know that products are being manufactured accurately to common standards and that their performance can be relied on.

Standards are another key component of the innovation process, providing guidance to the manufacturer on the expected quality and performance of a new product or process. And standards reassure the user that the product has been well tested before being launched onto the market. (See Box 9.)

Later in this block there is more about recent developments in manufacturing and the role of information and communication technologies in the transition from mass production to faster and more flexible systems.

Box 9 Standards and their role in innovation

Standards were originally related to units of measurement. The first 'standard' was the Egyptian royal cubit, which was made of black granite and was said to be equivalent to the length of the Pharoah's forearm and hand. This was also subdivided into finger, palm and hand widths – one 'small cubit' was equivalent to six palms. But because the human forearm was the master reference this meant that the cubit varied in different parts of the world. Over thousands of years agreement over units of measurement gradually spread. It was really industrialisation that brought a pressing need for better standards of measurement, both for parts of products and for manufacturing processes.

Essentially the incentive to standardise was economic. Standardised parts and methods of production meant that products could be made more accurately and efficiently, and the user could rely on their quality and performance with greater confidence. Furthermore maintenance and repair could be carried out more easily and cheaply by the replacement of one standardised part with another.

An early set of standards for the manufacture of a product were established in connection with steam boilers. Victorian engineers produced boilers of various shapes and sizes and therefore different performance characteristics. This resulted in uncertainty over how a particular boiler would perform and there were many boiler explosions and some deaths. There was pressure from insurance companies to reduce such risks by persuading engineers to conform to given standards for the manufacture of boilers and insurance cover was made conditional on compliance with manufacturing standards.

In 1901 the institutes for civil engineers, mechanical engineers, naval architects and the iron and steel industries formed a committee with the remit to standardise iron and steel sections for bridges, railways and shipping. One of the first standards was for tram rails, which led to a reduction in the number of different rails manufactured from 75 to 5. During the First World War standards were established that enabled aircraft to be made faster and that resulted in more reliable aircraft. In 1929 the standards committee became the British Engineering Standards Association and was granted a royal charter. Then in 1930 the association became the British Standards Institution (BSI) with a brief to oversee the establishing of national standards for the manufacture of a range of products. During the Second World War the standards for the manufacture of tins saved 40 000 tonnes of steel a year.

In 1947 the International Organization for Standardization (ISO) was founded to establish international standards for a wide range of industrial products.

Nowadays standards are agreed by committees drawn from government departments, research organisations, manufacturers and users. And standards aren't fixed but evolve to reflect changes in technology and society. By 2003 there were more than 14 000 international standards applying to film speeds, paper sizes, the dimensions of credit cards and the symbols on car dashboards. In the same year there were over 20 000 active British standards (1400 new standards were agreed in 2002 alone). As well as products, standards are developed to apply to ways of doing things – for example, the ISO 14000 series of international environmental management standards. Along with the information contained in patents, standards also represent a repository of know-how collected from wide experience of using products and processes. Some products in different countries nowadays are required by law to be tested against particular safety and performance standards before they can be offered for sale to the market. In the UK these include smoke alarms, emergency lighting, baby's dummies, fire extinguishers and fireworks. There are also many voluntary standards agreed upon by industries and trade associations because such standards can lead to more cost-effective production and maintenance, as well as greater customer confidence in the products concerned. For example the British Standard document (BS 1363:1995) for 13-amp fused plugs, socket-outlets, adaptors and connection units consists of four separate documents that specify the design, construction and performance characteristics of each product's components and details on how to test a new product design for compliance with the standard (Figure 79). The BSI Kitemark (itself a trade mark) shows that a product was initially tested and is regularly tested against appropriate standards. It has become a symbol of safety and quality for any product that carries it. Recently much effort has been devoted to agreeing standards for Europe's electrical plugs and sockets, so far without success.

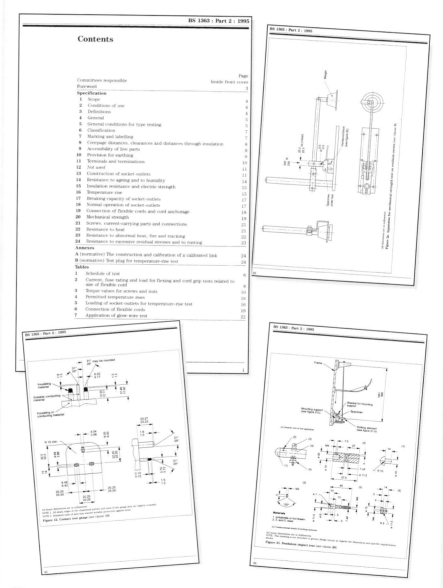

Figure 79   Extracts from British Standard BS 1363:Part 2:1995
Source: BSI

Increasingly the acceptance of certain standards, such as for the audio cassette in the 1960s and the compact disc in the 1980s, has helped manufacturers to avoid wasteful duplication. But in the past any agreement on standards has usually come only after a period of intense rivalry between manufacturers striving to have their technology accepted as the standard. Such confrontations have sometimes been so intense that they have been labelled 'format wars'. A classic example was the struggle between consumer electronics companies Sony and JVC for the video recording standard – Sony promoted the Betamax format and JVC the VHS format. Such battles can be fierce because the economic rewards of having a company's technology established as the international standard are enormous – just as the wasted production, development and marketing costs for the loser might be financially disastrous. Increasingly nowadays, however, much effort is devoted by groups of manufacturers, *before* expenditure on innovation has gone too far, to agree international standards and save themselves the expense of a format struggle. However innovation history has a habit of repeating itself. In 2003 two major groups of companies were lined up behind different standards for recordable DVDs. Hitachi, Panasonic, and Samsung supported DVD- (DVD minus) while Sony and Philips were behind the DVD+ (DVD plus) format. By the time you read this a common standard may (or may not) have been agreed. You may well be aware of more recent examples of such conflicts.

For more information on British and international standards you could visit the BSI and ISO websites.

What does the standard BS 8888:2004 cover? Do an internet search and find out.

3.2 Diffusion of innovations

Having managed to get an innovation manufactured and ready for the market, there are a number of factors that influence how well it will sell and how rapidly it is likely to diffuse:

- characteristics of the innovation itself

- nature of the market

- relevant government regulations.

3.2.1 Characteristics of the innovation

In one of the standard works in this field, Everett Rogers (2003) identifies five characteristics of an innovation that affect how quickly and to what extent it will sell:

1   relative advantage

2   compatibility

3   complexity

4   observability

5   trialability.

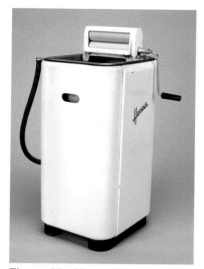

Figure 80   Hoover washing machine with wringer (model 0307), 1948 Source: Science & Society Picture Library

This was the first British-made compact machine of its type. It electricity heated the water and powered a contoured rotating disc, or pulsator, set into the side of the tub. Its distinctive features included a hand-operated wringer that could be folded down into the machine and a hose to remove the water after washing. The lid that covered the drum to prevent splashing could be attached to the other side of the wringer as a tray to receive the wrung clothes.

Figure 81   Rolls Duo-matic twin-tub, 1963, with the separate spin-dryer on the right Source: Science & Society Picture Library

Relative advantage

In order to succeed, an innovation has to be perceived as offering advantages relative to existing comparable products or services. For example it has more chance of selling if it is cheaper to make and buy, does the job better or does something previously not possible, offers more features, is easier to use, or is reliable and safe. Relative advantage is sometimes called competitive advantage.

For example the steady reduction in size and increase in efficiency of the electric motor encouraged the development of a range of labour-saving domestic appliances with rapid growth in the UK in the 1960s and 70s. Devices such as washing machines, vacuum cleaners and food mixers at first offered an obvious advantage to users in reducing the effort involved in carrying out domestic chores and they diffused widely. Each new generation of machines offered an advantage over the previous generation. So with electric washing machines in the UK by the 1950s many consumers had a basic tub with a revolving blade for washing and a pair of powered rollers fixed to the top of the machine for wringing out the water, which was actually invented 50 years earlier (Figure 80). Then by the 1960s there were twin-tubs with a washing tub and a separate spin-drying tub (Figure 81). By the 1970s the automatic washing machine (invented 40 years earlier) started to reach the mainstream (Figure 82), and by the 1990s these were usually microchip-controlled (invented 10–15 years earlier). Once the market was established the advantage of these products turned to offering more features for the same price. So there were, say, more wash programmes or greater temperature control or higher spin speeds for the money. And more recently attention has turned to washing machines that offer more energy efficiency in operation and reduced environmental impacts in manufacture, use and disposal. In order to maintain an advantage it's necessary to continuously improve the product. Look out for the latest improvements when you come to buy your next washing machine.

Compatibility

An innovation that is compatible with the *experiences, values and needs* of its potential buyers will be adopted more rapidly than one that isn't compatible. For example mobile phones have spread rapidly because they are compatible with social and cultural trends towards faster communications, increased personal mobility and the desirability of high-tech gadgets. However the car seat belt, patented in 1903, wasn't adopted on any significant scale until the 1970s (Figure 83). It took decades of increasing traffic and growing casualties in road accidents for safety to become a pressing concern, government to pass legislation and the seat belt to become a newly compatible innovation.

Complexity

If an innovation is perceived as difficult to use it will diffuse more slowly than one that is easy to understand. For example users of early personal computers needed an understanding of a programming language in order to use their machines. For most potential PC users this made the innovation too complex to consider buying. Then a graphical user interface was developed and incorporated by Apple Computer into the Lisa computer in 1983 (Figure 84) and more successfully into the Macintosh computer in 1984. Users could control

Figure 82   Hoover Keymatic washing machine, 1963 Source: Science & Society Picture Library

This is one of the new type of automatic washing machines that incorporated full wash, rinse and spin cycles and sold well in the late 1960s. The Hoover Keymatic featured a novel means of setting eight different wash programmes.

Figure 83   *Motor* magazine in 1960 advertises the car seat belt Source: John Frost Historical Newspaper Service

their computer by using a mouse to point at visible icons on a virtual desktop and software became simpler to use. This approach was taken up by newly emerging PC manufacturers and the rate of diffusion of the personal computer increased. Of course other factors contributed to the spread of the PC, such as falling cost, improved performance and more powerful software, but reduced complexity for users was a significant factor.

Figure 84   Apple Lisa launched in 1983 with the screen showing the graphical user interface Source: courtesy of Apple Computer Inc

Observability

The easier it is for people to see an innovation being used the more likely they are to consider buying it themselves. Examples include types of motor car, mobile phones and computers. Less obviously, products such as solar panels in domestic housing can sometimes be found in clusters on a housing estate (Figure 85). Innovations that are harder to see tend to diffuse more slowly, though there may well be other factors involved.

Figure 85   Making solar energy more observable – solar panels on the roof of terraced houses Source: Science Photo Library

Trialability

It helps to be able to try innovations before buying. While this isn't common for most innovations it can reduce any uncertainty the buyer might have about committing to a purchase and can increase the speed of diffusion. Buying a car usually involves a test drive that, although it probably isn't a fair reflection of the range of conditions under which the product will eventually be used, is better than nothing.

Encouraging diffusion

In general, innovations that are perceived as having relative advantages, being more compatible, less complex, observable, and trialable will diffuse more rapidly than other innovations.

3.2.2 Characteristics of consumers and the market

As well as the characteristics of an innovation affecting the extent of its take-up the nature of the market and the purchasing behaviour of consumers can influence success. Some people will always try to be among the first to buy a new product – Rogers (2003) calls people in this group *innovators* (Figure 86). They are typically young, affluent, well-informed, receptive to new ideas and willing to take risks. You probably know people who always seem to buy the latest gadget – it might even apply to you.

The innovator group and the next group, called *early adopters,* are often targeted by a company's launch publicity. However these first two groups are more often influenced by information gathered from friends and colleagues and from reviews of new products in the technical press, specialised publications and the internet.

To the frustration of everyone involved with producing innovations, the majority of consumers are more cautious and inclined to wait to see a product established with any performance problems solved. Rogers calls this group the *early majority* and it is the target of intensive advertising campaigns to increase the rate of a new product's diffusion. People's

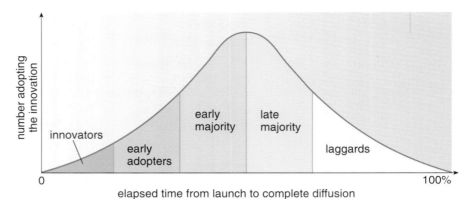

Figure 86 Rogers' diffusion curve showing five groups of consumer in relation to product diffusion

reticence is understandable, particularly with rapidly changing high-tech products. Who wants to be stuck with the latest equivalent of an eight-track audio cartridge or a Betamax video recorder?

Even more cautious consumers make up the group called the *late majority*, which tends to wait for the fall in price typical of mature products. The early and late majority tend to rely on the media and advertising for picking up information about a product.

Finally those in the *laggards* group buy a product close to the end of its life cycle, often shortly before it is replaced by a new, improved version of itself, or by something quite different. These last two consumer groups can also have economic reasons for delaying purchase.

There is also the question of timing. You saw above that some inventions can emerge before their time when the technology isn't sufficiently developed to deliver a reliable product. In other cases though, the inventive idea itself is okay and early products are satisfactory but it doesn't take off because the need for it is not yet established.

There have been a number of attempts to establish a market for the videophone over the last 50 years, with ever-increasing amounts of resources involved. In 2002 a few companies paid a staggering amount of money to acquire the operating licences for the so-called third generation of mobile telephony including video (£22 billion in the UK alone). Despite an intensive marketing campaign some mobile phone companies had only achieved around a tenth of their targeted market by 2004 and were nowhere near recouping the cost of the operating licence. (See Box 10.) Compared with the videophone the relatively simple second generation technology of short message service (text messaging) clearly tapped into a need that mobile users had. By May 2002 24 billion text messages were being sent each month and operators were getting between 10 and 20 per cent of their profits from text messaging.

Box 10   Diffusion of the videophone

The first experimental two-way videophone system was demonstrated in 1930 and linked the AT&T head office with its research department, which was called Bell Labs. In 1956 Bell Labs demonstrated its Picturephone system, which needed to use up to 125 telephone lines to achieve a reasonable picture. By 1968 Bell had improved the technology so that it would work with a relatively narrow bandwidth and finally the

Picturephone video telephone was introduced by Bell Labs as a commercial product in 1971.

The Picturephone was thought by many inside Bell Labs to be an example of a perfect innovation. It had overcome significant technical obstacles yet still met its production schedule and cost objectives. Market research had predicted slow acceptance followed by rapid growth. It was, however, a costly flop. Reasons suggested for its failure include high cost (rental of $125 per month) or that it was black and white at a time when consumers in the US were getting used to colour TV. Fundamentally though it failed because the market was not ready for it – some said it didn't offer enough of a competitive advantage over the telephone to justify its intrusiveness.

Meanwhile further technical developments in the videophone continued, particularly in Japan (Figure 87). By the mid-1990s videophones had been made more efficient by the development of data compression technology and once more were being offered for sale. Also at that time video links between personal computers were starting to become more common, exposing an increasing number of people to the idea of two-way visual communication. A new need was in the process of being cultivated, with huge rewards for the leading producers once a mass market could be established.

In recent years it seemed the mass market would be established with so-called third generation mobile telephony (Figure 87). This technology included the capacity for high-speed data exchange, mobile internet access and video streaming. The first licences for such services were awarded in 2002 but once again the market has been relatively slow to take up video telephony.

(a)

(b)

(c)

(d)

Figure 87   Different generations of videophone.
(a) Japanese TV telephone, the model 500 Viewphone, 1954 Source: Hulton Archive.
(b) Post Office video telephone, 1967 Source: courtesy of BT Archives.
(c) British Telecom videophone, 2002 Source: courtesy of BT (UK) Ltd.
(d) NEC third generation video mobile phone, 2003 Source: NEC 2001-2004, courtesy of NEC (UK) Ltd.

Of course in terms of the innovation process for third generation mobile telephony it's early days to be passing a judgement that the need doesn't exist on a sufficiently large scale or can't be encouraged to grow. Operators have had to cope with the teething troubles of an untried technology standard (imposed by European governments to ensure cross-border compatibility); colour screens and more ambitious operating requirements mean shorter battery lives; and purchase and service rental costs have been high, as they always are with a new technology and a small initial market. A common pattern would be for some of the early operators to withdraw from the market before the technology is improved, the need increases and the product becomes profitable and diffuses.

The diffusion of some innovations is encouraged by an existing infrastructure. The rapid spread of the telegraph was made possible because it was easy to string its wires alongside railway tracks, which provided a ready-made link between towns and cities. The telephone in turn was able to start by making use of the telegraph network, although it had to add many extra elements such as links to individual homes. You saw in Section 1 how the development of the modern business corporation created the need for inventions such as the typewriter and the telephone to improve the speed and efficiency of communications.

Some inventions rely for their diffusion on developments in related technological innovations or systems. A method of audio compression known as MP3 was originally developed as part of the system used for high-definition TV transmission and digital satellite systems. MP3 is a standard (see Box 9) that is part of a set published by the Motion Picture Experts Group. By ignoring audio content outside of the range of frequencies normally audible to humans, MPEG compression produces sound quality that is good enough and it results in a file of digital audio that is much smaller than previous sound files.

MP3 players started appearing in the early 1990s as separate audio players but didn't arouse much interest. The need for personal, portable audio was met at the time by cassette players and, increasingly through the 1990s, CD players. It took innovation in other areas to create the conditions that led to a growing interest in MP3 innovations. These areas included the increasing access to personal computers, the growth of the internet, the improvement in storage capacity of digital devices and the development of file-sharing software (see Box 11).

Box 11   MP3's diffusion depended on innovations in related areas

As well as being small and portable, MP3 devices have a number of additional competitive advantages. Digital compression allows the size of recordings to be significantly smaller without noticeable loss of sound quality so the capacity of portable devices can be much greater. Compatibility with computer systems means that music can be acquired from the internet or from a CD and easily manipulated into a sequence desired by the user.

Although MP3 players had been around for a number of years it wasn't until 1998 when Winamp was offered on the internet as a free music player that the MP3 craze started to take off. This was given a boost in 1999 by the appearance of a website called Napster. Napster offered file-sharing software that allowed individuals to access each other's hard drives and thereby exchange their digital music collections. This so-called peer-to-peer communication created a virtual community of music enthusiasts that grew rapidly.

In the past the copying of music with audio recorders wasn't highly visible and the recording technology could be used legitimately in ways that didn't involve any infringement of copyright. So the recording industry had no effective means of preventing infringement and settled for receiving a royalty from manufacturers of recording devices.

However with Napster using a public forum such as the internet to encourage the 'theft' of intellectual property the recording industry acted to have it shut down for encouraging copyright violation. Napster was ordered to cease operating in 2001 by a US court following a lawsuit brought by the Recording Industry Association of America. Napster was subsequently relaunched as a commercial MP3 provider but even before its closure it had become clear that there was a large market for MP3 audio. Users of file-sharing software quickly found alternative sources for swapping music and by 2003 unauthorised downloads of songs across the internet was estimated to be around 2 billion per month.

But the commercial sector had noticed the activities of these MP3 innovators and it wasn't long before a kind of official infrastructure started to appear. Apple launched its iTunes Music Store with 500 000 songs in 2003 in collaboration with the major music companies, mainly to boost the sales of its new iPod player (Figure 88). The availability of legitimate downloadable music helped the iPod to become the most popular electronic gadget bought on both sides of the Atlantic that Christmas. Other companies planned to follow Apple's example in 2004, including Sony, Microsoft, Coca-Cola and Wal-Mart. Like Apple these companies are not just interested in making money from selling music but also hope to use this innovation to sell others such as MP3 players, music editing software and so on. The diffusion of one innovation can help sell another.

Figure 88   Apple's iPod player

3.2.3 Government regulations and legislation

You saw above in Section 2 how governments can stimulate invention by providing incentives for manufacturers to develop new products. The example given was in the field of alternative fuel vehicles in the USA and Europe. As well as influencing the development of innovations, government legislation and regulations can also affect diffusion by creating conditions that encourage consumers to buy and use particular innovations.

In the UK the government has introduced a mixture of incentives to encourage the wider use of less polluting vehicles. Since March 2001 the levels of vehicle excise duty and company car tax for new vehicles have been linked to the carbon dioxide emissions of each model of vehicle rather than to the engine size. In addition lower taxation levels are applied to alternative fuels such as liquefied petroleum gas (LPG) or compressed natural gas (CNG) compared with petrol and diesel. Low-emission, alternative fuel vehicles are currently (2005) exempt from the central London congestion charge, which has already brought about an increase in drivers and fleet managers opting for LPG or CNG conversions and a slow but steady increase in the use of such vehicles.

> Taking personal audio products as an example, where are you on Rogers' diffusion curve? Are you in with the innovators, early adopters, early majority, late majority or laggards?

3.3 Sustaining and disruptive innovation

Once an innovation starts diffusing into the marketplace it can have differing degrees of impact. As mentioned in Section 1, although innovations generally offer progress, there are some that complement existing ways of doing things and some that are more dramatic in their impact. In his book called *The Innovator's Dilemma* Clayton M. Christensen (2003) labels these two types of innovation sustaining and disruptive.

Sustaining innovations are those that improve the performance of established products so they meet the needs of most current customers – perhaps making the products more reliable, faster or cheaper. Such innovations can be incremental or radical in their nature but usually have a sustaining effect for leading firms in a given industry. For example successive innovations in the provision of conventional telephone equipment and services served to sustain the major players – such as British Telecom and Cable & Wireless in the UK – in their market position. However the arrival of mobile telephones proved to be a disruptive innovation in the field of telecommunications and younger companies – such as Motorola, Ericsson, Nokia – exploited this new market.

Disruptive technologies usually introduce a new way of operating in a particular market sector that challenges existing companies to decide whether to ignore or embrace such new developments. You saw above that innovations often under-perform in their early incarnations. Compared with conventional mature products they may seem unpromising to existing companies. However such innovations can have other features that some existing and many new customers value. Christensen (2003, p. xviii) put forward the view that,

> Products based on disruptive technologies are typically cheaper, simpler, smaller, and frequently more convenient to use.

Sometimes these disruptive innovations go on to capture new as well as current customers to the extent that they rival or in some cases surpass the market for the existing technology. Examples include photocopying (compared with carbon paper copying), digital photography (compared with chemical film processing), online retailing (compared with face-to-face shopping) and even distance learning (compared with classroom-based learning).

Companies regularly listen to their best customers and tend to develop new products based on the immediate promise of profitability and growth. These companies are often not able to build a case for investing in disruptive technologies until it's too late because:

- Disruptive innovations are simpler and cheaper, promising lower profit margins.

- Disruptive innovations are usually first commercialised in emerging markets that are often perceived as insignificant.

- Leading firms' most profit-conscious customers are generally tied in to existing successful products and don't want that disrupted.

According to Christensen the 'innovator's dilemma' is that outstanding companies can do everything right – such as listen carefully to their customers or invest heavily in new technologies – but still lose their market leadership. They miss 'the next great wave' unless they know when to abandon traditional business practices in the face of certain types of market and technology change. For example IBM dominated the mainframe computer market but missed the emergence of the simpler minicomputer. A company called DEC created the minicomputer market (Figure 89) along with Hewlett-Packard and others but they all missed the desktop personal computer market that was captured by Apple, Commodore, Compaq and IBM's new independent PC division. For many years Xerox dominated the market for large-volume photocopiers used in copy centres but missed out on the huge market for small tabletop office photocopiers, ending up as only a minor player.

> There are times when it's right *not* to listen to customers, right to invest in developing lower-performance products that promise *lower* margins, and right to aggressively pursue small, rather than substantial, markets.

(Christensen, 2003, p. xv)

Disruptive technologies tend to lead to new markets with significant advantages for companies who enter the market early. But large established companies need to ensure a level of growth not possible in the early stages of a new, small market – even though often that new market will become large in the future. Often, established companies adopt a strategy of waiting to see if the market will grow sufficiently large to deliver the sales they need. However then they run the risk of being too far behind early entrants to catch up. Those who have

Figure 89   DEC's first minicomputer (1965) was a disruptive innovation for the big mainframe computer companies like IBM Source: Science & Society Picture Library

succeeded have tended to devolve the responsibility for commercialising the disruptive technology to a smaller offshoot organisation that can respond more easily to the opportunities for growth in a small market – like with IBM's PC division.

Part of the innovator's dilemma is that with disruptive innovation there are clear advantages to entering the market early but it's largely unknown territory. Companies can't have market data if little or none exists or make financial projections when they don't know likely income or costs. Companies poised to market a disruptive innovation have to keep a close watch on the market and their competitors, be ready to act quickly to change their product if necessary and be prepared to take risks.

Even the desire of established companies to try to improve their products to maintain competitive advantage over their rivals can work against them. For example the rate of improved performance offered by computer manufacturers has grown faster than most computer users' needs. Accordingly the performance of mainframe computers grew to exceed the data processing requirements of many of their customers, who were able to have their needs met by simpler and cheaper desktop machines linked to devices that stored the data.

> When the performance of two or more competing products has improved beyond what the market demands, customers can no longer base their choice upon which is the higher performing product. The basis of product choice often evolves from functionality to reliability, then to convenience, and, ultimately, to price.

(Christensen, 2003. p. xxviii)

Christensen says that companies need to discover how their mainstream customers *use* their products in order to be able to identify the points at which this basis of competition changes. Then they can act quickly to defend themselves against competitors entering the market with disruptive innovations.

Other than the examples given, can you think of a disruptive technology leading to a new market?

The domestic video cassette recorder introduced into the UK in the late 1970s could be considered a disruptive technology. It challenged TV and film companies to create video versions of their products, encouraged a new rental industry to start up and spawned innovations in technology for home entertainment.

3.4   Phases and waves of innovation

To wrap up this section I'll take a broad look at the innovation process. It's possible to think of innovation at different levels of generalisation. There are individual stages that innovations go through from invention to diffusion – these are sometimes called *phases*. At a higher level of generalisation each complete set of phases for a group of related technologies can be seen as a *wave*. Sometimes such waves appear close together and combine to have a revolutionary impact.

In another classic book, *Mastering the Dynamics of Innovation*, James Utterback (1994) identifies three overall phases in the innovation process: *emerging*, *growth* and *maturity*. In the case of disruptive innovations the *emerging* phase is characterised by radical new products and the appearance of completely new industrial sectors. In the past, for example, a new sector emerged around electronics. More recently information and communication technology and biotechnology sectors have also emerged. During this emerging phase many new companies appear, ready and willing to exploit the new products. They tend to be small, science-based and entrepreneurial, prepared to take risks in a highly uncertain new market. To start with they compete by producing specialised products tailored to the needs of a small group of customers. There are often frequent product changes as the sector struggles to perfect the new technology.

During the *growth* phase technological uncertainty is reduced, sector-wide standards appear and dominant designs emerge. This leads to an increase in output usually accompanied by investment in specialised production equipment. The focus for companies also turns to making changes that differentiate their products from those of their competitors. Increasing production costs and failure to compete on product performance and features can cause some firms to drop out of the sector – particularly if they are out-of-step with the sector's standard designs.

In the *mature* phase the main drivers are volume and cost. The focus is now on process innovation to reduce costs and investment in special-purpose, often automated, equipment makes it costly to remain in the sector. A small number of companies dominate what is now a major market and the pace of change slows.

Utterback observes that the history of a particular industrial sector doesn't necessarily end with the mature phase. Evolution can continue with further waves of technological change. Radical innovations can still appear from inside or outside the industry sector or sometimes from collaboration with other industries. In subsequent waves of innovation the tendency is for markets to become more highly defined with entrenched firms and fixed distribution channels, all of which reduce the chances of further radical innovation or significant reform of the industry. What often happens next is that a disruptive innovation comes along and sets off a whole new wave. I'll look at two of these new waves later.

You've already seen that innovations can involve differing degrees of technological change and seen the impact upon the socio-economic system. At the lowest level *incremental innovations* involve small-scale improvements, from a company making the manufacturing process more efficient or making changes to an existing product in response to feedback from users, to an inventor coming up with an idea that improves upon existing products. These innovations do not have a dramatic impact on the society that uses them but they do lead to steady improvements in the efficiency of manufacture, and the variety, quality and performance of products.

Radical innovations are more significant new steps that could not have arisen from incremental improvements to existing technology. They do have a more widespread impact in that they often involve a combination of product, process and organisational innovation. In Section 2 you saw how Chester Carlson's invention of xerography ultimately led to the establishment of a new photocopying industry.

Technology system changes occur when technological and organisational innovations combine to affect several sectors of the economy. So the automation of many aspects of production and assembly had a significant impact on a range of industries.

Finally there is a level of change that has a widespread impact on almost every aspect of an economy and even on the way society organises itself. Some theorists call this a change in the techno-economic regime, others a *technological revolution*. This involves changes in the dominant technologies, production methods and the associated patterns of social organisation that often characterise an era. The first technological revolution was based on innovations in steam power that resulted in industrialisation and people moving home to work in factories. Later revolutions have been based around innovations in electricity, chemistry, electronics, microelectronics, computing, telecommunications, biotechnology and nanotechnology.

I think the pace of change and the complexity of our relationship with technology are increasing. Do you agree or disagree? But what are the implications of this for the twenty-first century? In the next two sections I plan to look at two aspects of the growth of innovation that seem to have particular significance. In Section 4 I'll consider whether there's still a role for the individual inventor, given the growing complexity of technology and the need for increasingly specialised knowledge and skills. Then in Section 5 I'll examine the increasing impact of new science-based technologies such as ICT and nanotechnology.

SAQ 8

A dramatic example of the importance of process innovation for a product's success is mentioned in subsection 1.1 of this block. What is it?

SAQ 9

Rogers gives five characteristics of an innovation that affect how well it will sell and how quickly it will diffuse. Briefly use these characteristics to explain the rapid diffusion of the mobile phone.

SAQ 10

Would you classify the following as examples of sustaining innovation or disruptive innovation?

(a) cordless domestic phones

(b) mobile phones

(c) Edison's electric light

(d) compact fluorescent lamps.

Key points of Section 3

- To succeed in bringing an invention to the market there are technical, financial and organisational obstacles to overcome.

- Choosing appropriate materials and manufacturing processes for a particular new product is an important aspect of the innovation process. Environmental impacts and sustainability play a part in the choice of materials and processes.

- Rogers' characteristics of an innovation can affect how well it will sell and how quickly it will diffuse. He named the characteristics relative advantage, compatibility, complexity, observability and trialability.

- Rogers' characteristics of the consumers can also affect diffusion. He named the consumer groups innovators, early adopters, early majority, late majority and laggards.

- Government regulations can also be effective in providing incentives for manufacturers to develop new products and encouraging consumers to buy and use innovations.

- Sustaining innovations offer improvements to the performance of established products and have a sustaining effect for firms. Disruptive innovations involve a new way of operating in a particular market, challenging existing companies to decide whether to ignore or embrace such new developments.

- Utterback identifies three overall phases in the innovation process: emerging, growth and maturity.

The key points for Section 3 meet learning outcomes 1.1, 1.8, 1.9, 1.10, 1.11, 2.1, 2.2, 2.3 and 2.4.

4 Decline of the individual inventor?

Though it is difficult to be precise about this it has been calculated that by 2000 around 20 per cent of patents were being assigned to individuals, while 80 per cent were assigned to companies. A century ago these figures would have been reversed. As technology has become more complex and knowledge and skills more specialised, it is argued that examples of successful individual inventors have become less common while the role of research and development teams inside organisations has grown in importance. So do individuals still have a role to play in the modern innovation process? I'll start by looking at some of the problems faced by inventive individuals and at the nature of their relationship with organisations.

The DVD contains several examples of individual inventors who have appeared on the BBC's *Best Inventions* and *Innovation Nation* TV programmes. The clips offer an insight into some of the obstacles and opportunities facing individual inventors.

4.1 Lone inventors

Some individuals who start out on their own are true lone inventors because they have no contact with others in a particular field of technology. However they usually have some experience of using a particular product or process themselves and have observed their own or other people's problems. They then spend a period thinking about improvements to existing devices or they might have spotted what they feel is a gap in the market that can be met by a new product.

Even lone inventors though cannot avoid having to deal with others for long. They need to test the reaction of other people to their inventive ideas and make appropriate refinements in response to feedback. Then, unless the inventors themselves have unlimited resources, they will need to liaise with others in order to fund any further prototype development that might be necessary before full-scale manufacture is possible. To achieve this they need the help of those who have access to, or who can find, resources – entrepreneurs, financiers or existing organisations operating in a relevant area of technology. It is rare for individual inventors to achieve large-scale manufacture of their inventions. However there are exceptions.

Exercise 2   Anywayup cup

I want you to read an account, in her own words, of how Mandy Haberman (Figure 90) developed an idea into a product whose worldwide annual sales in 2005 were 10 million units. As you read through this account make notes on how it exemplifies invention and innovation introduced in Sections 2 and 3 above. Specifically think about how it illustrates:

1   motivations for invention

2   the Usher–Lawson, five-stage invention process

3   overcoming technical, financial and organisational obstacles to innovation

4   how Rogers' characteristics of innovation might account for this product's successful diffusion

5   lessons for the individual inventor and innovator.

(a)   (b)

Figure 90   (a) Mandy Haberman and her range of Anywayup cups. (b) The effectiveness of the leak-proof valve being demonstrated. Source: courtesy of Mandy Haberman

Haberman started inventing in 1980 when her daughter was born with a condition that made feeding difficult. Haberman designed a feeder bottle for children with sucking problems. As with many inventors she didn't stop there.

In the beginning

I first had the idea for a totally non-drip trainer cup that would seal between sips in the summer of 1990. It was the school holidays of August 1990 and my daughter, Emily, had been invited to play at her friend's house. When I went to collect her, the little boy's aunt was there with her toddler. The toddler was drinking from a conventional trainer cup as she was walking around the lounge. The house was beautifully furnished and his aunt was keeping a watchful eye in case the toddler dropped her cup. When the cup fell, she dived to catch it before it hit the floor. Seeing her constant state of stress and the gymnastic feats required to prevent Ribena stains on the carpet made me think that it must be possible to make a cup that would seal between sips.

The only cups that I was aware of at that time that sealed at all, were travel cups such as the Tommee Tippee Sip n Seal, which the mother had to turn to seal after the toddler had finished with it. Apart from that there were cups with separate travel lids but nothing that automatically sealed between sips. I started to think about the problem and had the idea for a diaphragm that would fit between the lid and base of a normal trainer cup. The diaphragm would have a valve to let drink out, located under the lid-spout, and another valve to let air in, located under the lid air hole.

How I went about it

Although I could make 'kitchen sink' models with bits and pieces stuck together, I had no proper equipment for producing prototypes, so I contacted a friend and colleague, Jim Hennequin of Airmuscle Limited, who had done work for me from time to time in the past. Jim came to my house to discuss the project in the first week of November 1990 and we arranged to have some simple tools made.

The first prototype consisted of a standard cup base, a custom-made lid (vacuum-formed plastic) with a large, single hole in the spout, and a flexible, moulded diaphragm with a thickened rim and two domed, slit-cut valves. The thickened rim would form an O-ring seal between the cup base and the lid. The big valve, located under the spout, would open when the spout was sucked, releasing liquid out through the spout. The smaller valve would open and let air back in under the pull of vacuum within the cup. But the vacuum tended to pull the valves away from their locations. We overcame this by making a supporting disc to hold the diaphragm in position. Also the lid tended to bump up on initial assembly because of compressed air in the cup. We overcame this by rigging up a metal clip to secure the lid.

These were all minor problems that could be easily overcome. However, there was a more fundamental problem. This was that after liquid was sucked through the valve, not all the liquid passed out of the hole in the spout. This residue then dripped if the cup was inverted and shaken. Despite all the above failings this prototype did prove the concept worked.

I made a lot of further development prototypes, including some from cold cure latex rubber cast into the form of the lid-spout, I hoped to be rid of the gap between valve and spout so that liquid would not be retained. However, I could not overcome the problem completely. I wanted my product to be totally drip-proof so I was not satisfied with these results. I decided the only way to overcome the problem completely would be if the valve opening was not enclosed within the spout but released liquid directly into the mouth.

Eureka

Finally, at 4.30 one morning, I had a flash of inspiration. In the course of materials research for another project, I had come across a soft, flexible plastic that could be moulded directly onto rigid plastic. Now I could see how to create a rigid trainer cup spout with a flexible valve directly at its top surface, therefore solving the problems of residue completely. This also had the advantages of requiring no assembly and of being extremely easy to clean.

Before spending a lot of money on tooling, I wanted try the idea out by simulation. It was not possible to glue the materials together so I made a working rig using sandwiches of materials with the edges smeared liberally with Vaseline to simulate a one-piece component. The model proved the theory.

Going out into the world

I had applied for a patent in 1992 (Figure 91) and over a period of years had shown my prototypes to about 20 companies. Despite already having applied for my patent, I was very aware of how cut-throat big businesses are. So in addition to having patent protection, I also got them to sign confidentiality agreements.

Responses varied. At one company I chucked a cup full of juice onto the director's desk, right on top of all his papers. Thank God, it didn't spill a drop! He was impressed, once he'd recovered from the shock. However, his enthusiasm eventually waned when he realised that he wasn't going to get something for nothing. Typically, companies wanted to hold on to the prototypes while they assessed the product. Months would tick by and I would

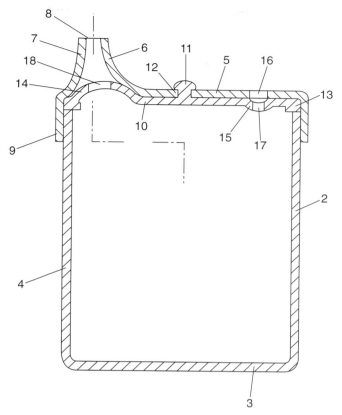

Figure 91 Drawing from Mandy Haberman's drinks container patent Source: adapted from patent GB 2 266 045 A

(The following is from the patent document and shows the kind of language used in patents.) A drinking vessel suitable for use as a trainer cup or cup for the elderly comprises an open-mouthed generally cup-shaped container (2) and a lid (5) for covering the open mouth of the container (2). The lid (5) has an associated mouthpiece (6). Valve means (10) are provided to prevent flow of liquid from the interior of the container (2) through the mouthpiece (6) unless a predetermined level of lip pressure and suction is applied to the mouthpiece (6).

become very twitchy about it (generally with due reason) until finally I would demand their return.

Those that were interested, were either not prepared to make financial commitment or were not prepared to commit to the sort of minimum sales figures that I considered appropriate. I was confident that the product would be very successful, therefore I decided to invest my own money in further tooling. I believed in it and was prepared to put my hand deeper into my pocket to prove it.

A word from the wise to anyone trying to license an invention – *never* leave samples with *anyone*. Companies who are full of enthusiasm, take your samples and then go quiet are *ripping you off*!

Taking the initiative

I had proper prototypes made that looked and behaved like a manufactured product. They were leak proof – when filled and inverted, they could withstand vigorous shaking for 10 seconds. They could also be turned upside down and left overnight. In fact my cups could be left for weeks on end in this position without spilling a drop.

The next challenge was to find the right people to help me bring it to market. Thanks to a chance introduction through someone who knew someone who knew somebody else, I made contact with a small Cardiff based company, called V&A Marketing Ltd. It was basically a two-man band with a couple of office staff that was on the lookout for new ideas to run with. I contacted the company.

To assess market response to the cup, V&A (named after Vic and Adrian) suggested I took an exhibition stand at the Nursery Exhibition in a few months time. I spent about £5000 hurriedly having a stand designed and equipped. Shortly before the show I telephoned Vic to discuss the hotel arrangements for Olympia. Imagine my horror when he said, 'Why Olympia? The show is at Earls Court'. I had booked the wrong show. It turned out that I was meant to book The Baby and Child Fair, which is a trade fair. The Nursery World show was more educational – for nursery and creche organisers. After feeling exceedingly sick, I decided that because we would lose a lot of money if we cancelled, we would just have to do both shows.

At the exhibitions we showed prototypes that were convincing as real product samples. These consisted of my own valved lids on standard cup bases. These had had printed designs when I bought them, which I had gently sanded off with wet-or-dry paper. As part of our display we had an eye catching mobile hanging over people's heads made from upside-down cups full of coloured liquid. We demonstrated the effectiveness of our samples by one moment drinking from them, and the next moment vigorously shaking them over people's clothes! The shows were a huge success; the crowds on our stand kept blocking the aisles. All together, we took about £10 000 of advance orders. With this money as capital I was able to purchase proper production tooling.

I formed The Haberman Company Ltd and we rocketed into business. It took us about 3 months to fulfil the orders we had taken at the shows but, such was the demand for the product, we lost orders for only about three or four cups. We realised that we needed to get the product into the supermarkets but this was not going to be easy. They don't like to do business with one-product companies. Then we had a brain wave. Having already been turned down by Tesco, we decided we had nothing to lose. We filled a cup with concentrated Ribena, and put it loose inside a white box, and posted it to the buyer! A few days later, the telephone rang – we were into Tesco!

From little acorns

In 1997 we launched a new range, designed by Sebastian Conran and, under licence, in July 1998, V&A set up its own manufacturing facility so that all business was run from under one roof. Since then we've never looked back. In our first year 1996, we achieved sales of 500 000 units, which grew to 750 000 in 1997. Between my licensees in America and V&A in the UK, annual sales of 7–10 million cups are now achieved. We have distributors selling into 70 countries worldwide. The Anywayup cup is a Millennium product and has won many awards including the Design Business Association design effectiveness awards for innovation and product design. I was also awarded the title British female inventor of the year for 2000. V&A Marketing was judged the fastest growing business in Wales in 1999. While the Anywayup cup is still the mainstay of its production, V&A now offers a full range of products.

Now, instead of having to interest companies in the product, I have to sue them for infringement. But I guess that is the price you have to pay for success. We are now a name to be reckoned with in the industry. The man whose desk I chucked the cup onto, has been in touch with us several times to persuade us to grant him a licence. Sorry, mate – no chance.

(Haberman, 2002)

As Haberman said in passing in the above article her Anywayup cup had already captured a significant share of the trainer-cup market when the makers of the Tommy Tippee brand launched a cup recognisably similar to the prototype she'd shown them some years before. Having brand-name clout, Tommy Tippee quickly took two-thirds of her sales. At the risk of losing her house Haberman and her licensee started legal proceedings. In a *Sunday Times* report Haberman said,

> But as it got nearer the court date, they said, 'Let's have a meeting.' That's what infringers do. Wait until you go broke or cave in, or offer to settle on the courthouse steps. But we couldn't settle.

> The factory was up to its eyes in debt for new machinery, and was employing 70 people. It was win or bust. My insurance only covered a drop in the ocean. But we won. They appealed, of course, and again they took us all the way, and settled out of court at the eleventh hour. There's so little protection, it's naive. Nobody's prepared to stand behind you through the enforcement process.

(Martin, 2002)

Discussion

1 Motivations for invention

These appear to be a mixture of constructive discontent (trainer cups causing spills) technical curiosity (how to make a cup that would seal between sips) a desire to make money (having identified a gap in the market) and a desire to help people (the nervous aunt).

2 The Usher–Lawson, five-stage invention process

Identification of the problem occurred when visiting the house of her daughter's friend and by reviewing current products. *Exploration* involved the solution-focused strategy of making, testing and refining prototypes. An *act of insight* occurred in this case when Haberman remembered a soft, flexible plastic used on a previous project and realised it could be adapted to help provide a solution for her trainer cup. *Critical revision* involved moving from this act of insight to a working invention. Initially Haberman made a prototype that 'looked and behaved like a manufactured product' for the purpose of demonstrating the product to potential buyers then this became the basis for the finished product offered for sale. The product was subsequently improved through better design, winning several awards as well as achieving increased sales.

3 Overcoming technical, financial and organisational obstacles to innovation

Haberman gives a brief account of the process of overcoming the key *technical* obstacle of perfecting a one-way, non-drip valve. This included choosing the right materials for a rigid spout and flexible valve combination for the prototype and later choosing the most appropriate tooling and manufacturing process for large-scale production.

Financial obstacles are especially difficult to overcome for individuals. After her initial investment paid for prototypes and early marketing of the cup, Haberman got the boost she needed by being able to set up a production process with the money she took in advance orders.

Organisational obstacles proved more difficult to overcome as no existing organisation was willing to take on production of the cup (remember the not-invented-here attitude) so Haberman went into business for herself (as an inventor-entrepreneur).

4   How Rogers' characteristics of innovation might account for this product's successful diffusion

Relative advantage – The new trainer cup didn't drip or spill, which gave it a significant advantage over rival products and an obvious selling point.

Compatibility – Because the cup didn't spill it was compatible with the values of minimising the mess caused by children. Because the cup was brightly coloured, had no sharp edges and was simple to use, it was compatible with other products intended for robust use by children.

Complexity – The trainer cup was easy to understand and use, which contributed to its sales.

Observability – The product would have been seen being used by 'innovators' or 'early adopters', which would have encouraged further sales.

Trialability – Early versions of the product were trialable at exhibitions but, as with many innovations, this was not possible before purchase, so it wasn't a factor in its diffusion.

5   Lessons for the individual inventor and innovator

Innovation carries a big financial risk for individuals (you could lose your house).

If you are prepared to take the risk and can prove there's a market for your product then commercial companies might start to take an interest and resources might follow (remember Hickman and the Workmate).

Taking out some form of protection for your idea, such as a patent, is generally recommended. However, while this might work as a deterrent to copying, if a company does infringe your patent it will be expensive for an individual to carry out a successful prosecution through the courts (remember Hickman's £1m court costs).

Individuals should be careful in their dealings with commercial organisations. Haberman isn't the first inventor to have felt uneasy leaving a prototype with a company for assessment. She was wise to get them to sign a confidentiality agreement first. The resolution of any dispute often comes down to financial muscle and nerve.

Individuals need to be prepared to admit they don't know everything and seek specialist help where appropriate. Haberman sought the help of Airmuscle Ltd. with the tooling to make prototypes, V&A to help her with marketing, and Sebastian Conran to help her with design.

Some companies are inundated with ideas for products from individual inventors. It can be a good idea to think of some way to make your product stand out from the crowd. Posting a cup full of Ribena loose inside a white box got the attention of Tesco.

Individuals need to be determined and persistent in the face of the obstacles they will encounter in bringing a product to market.

For every success story, however, there are many more stories of frustration and eventual failure. Kane Kramer was a lone inventor who filed a patent application (GB2115996) in 1981 for a solid-state 'portable data processing and storage system' said to be the forerunner of the MP3 player. Like several of the early telephone inventors mentioned in Section 1 Kramer had to let his patent lapse through lack of financial support. This is a common fate for individual inventors.

Over the years there have been repeated efforts to set up an infrastructure to help inventive individuals and small firms to develop their ideas into commercial innovations. The NRDC, which helped with the development of the hovercraft in the 1950s, was an early example. Since then there have been regular government schemes to encourage individuals to get involved in innovation – for example in the UK currently the Department of Trade and Industry offers a range of support for individuals and small businesses. There are also private firms, such as the British Technology Group, prepared to help commercialise inventions. Some universities support local inventors by offering facilities for the development of prototypes. And there are inventors' clubs in some parts of the UK.

But it's sometimes difficult to pitch this help early enough in the innovation process and to reach lone inventors before they become discouraged and give up. And even if an individual gets as far as developing and perhaps patenting a prototype, there are still many barriers for lone inventors to overcome.

4.2   Inventors and organisations

You saw above that the relationship between a lone inventor and those organisations whose help is needed to develop the invention into an innovation can be problematic. In the case of Mandy Haberman and her Anywayup cup she couldn't persuade any existing organisations to invest in her invention so had to go it alone. But even when individual inventors succeed in persuading an organisation to commercialise their invention there can be problems in the relationship. Like Haberman the next example is of an individual who managed to see his inventive idea transformed into a mass-market innovation. However on the way the individual inventor had to accept some compromise to his original vision in the face of manufacturing and commercial constraints imposed by the organisation that took up his idea.

4.2.1   Rubber-fin soccer boot

Craig Johnston was an Australian who played football for Liverpool in the 1980s. After his retirement in 1988 he was approached by a boot manufacturer to endorse a top-of-the-range product made from kangaroo skin. Craig refused and set out to design a cheap boot for children and adults that would have its own larger, flatter, sweet spot for better accuracy and be made of something other than leather to give better grip to increase control. The sweet spot is the area in the centre of the top surface of the boot that makes contact with the ball. A fatter sweet spot reduces the deviation of the ball and increases its velocity.

Craig took existing boots and tried attaching a number of different materials such as serrated plastic from a conveyor belt. Then, when windsurfing one day, he noticed the thermoplastic-rubber shoes he'd borrowed gave excellent grip in the wet – a quality he wanted for his football boot. He persuaded the French manufacturer Okespur to produce a prototype boot from the same material with a flattened top surface to give a larger area of contact with the ball.

He flew to France to test the prototype, but he was disappointed with the results and thought about changes he could make. That evening in his hotel room he borrowed an engraver's tool and started etching 'tread-marks' into the surface of the boot in an attempt to improve the grip (Figure 92). The next morning he tried out the boot again and discovered that although he had improved the grip it was at the expense of power and control.

After 3 or 4 months of further experimenting, what Johnston called 'cut and try', he developed a version with a series of protruding fins that was closer to what he wanted. Then by chance he noticed a plug of rubber bounce when dropped on Okespur's factory floor and had the idea of trying the sort of rubber used in the superballs children play with – it's a material called polybutadiene. Craig then consulted the Malaysian Rubber Producers Research Association, which advised him that polybutadiene tore easily and that he'd be better using natural rubber with some of its properties manipulated for greater rebound. However such a procedure required vulcanisation, which was not possible with any of Okespur's injection moulding machines. So Craig got them to make a flat mould of this material, to the fin design, and stitch it to a conventional boot. The results were exactly what he wanted.

By this time the project had cost Craig £250 000. He had patented the rubber fin design but needed help to go any further. He took it to FIFA, soccer's international rule-makers, to check that it would be legal. Having got FIFA's approval he approached Adidas in Germany to discuss the potential for manufacture.

The rubber fins and bumps were what had made Craig's prototype work but Adidas wanted their product to look less like a rubber hedgehog and more like a normal soccer boot. The company whittled down the new rubber sweet spot area, confining the fins to a small section of the toe. Craig initially resisted but eventually a compromise was reached. Adidas named the new boot the Predator.

There was still a lot of best kangaroo leather in the Predator, which was something of a sore point for Craig. And instead of a cheap coaching aid the Predator was one of the most expensive boots ever made. Adidas decided to pitch the boot at the top end of the market. The Predator was unveiled on 17 December 1993 – just 48 hours before the World Cup finals draw. It went on sale in the UK in May 1994 at £120 (Figures 93 and 94).

4.2.2 User turned inventor

Craig Johnston's part in the development of the Predator is an example of how using a product, the standard football boot, can lead to ideas for its improvement. It's impossible to be certain but this idea might never have emerged from within the various companies manufacturing football boots. It took a special kind of user to come up with the idea and develop it into a prototype. This also shows how an individual inventor with no prior specialist knowledge can take an inventive idea quite some way towards innovation but that this can be costly – £250 000 in this case. To go further requires a level of resources usually only available to an established firm. It would be a bigger step for an individual to set up a new firm to exploit an invention. It is less costly and risky to have the idea taken up by a company already working in that field. One of the obstacles here, though, is of resistance to a new

Figure 92 Craig Johnston using an engraver's tool to etch 'tread-marks' on a prototype boot Source: BBC Education

Figure 93   Craig Johnston and the Adidas Predator football boot after launch Source: BBC Education

Figure 94   Adidas Predator football boot in 2004 – note the evolution of the design Source: Reuters

product from outside that challenges a firm's existing products – the not-invented-here attitude.

The example also shows the role of chance in invention – when Johnston observed the rubber plug bouncing on the factory floor. And the inventor made unexpected connections between car tyres, toy superballs and football boots that led to a breakthrough act of insight. As you saw earlier 'chance favours only the prepared mind' and Craig Johnston's mind was busy searching for solutions to his technical problems. At this stage Johnston placed a great reliance on the cut-and-try approach, spending hours carving tread patterns in the prototype boots. Invention can only proceed so far with cut-and-try methods though. Specialist scientific knowledge was needed to provide a fuller understanding of the behavioural characteristics of the product and the best way of maximising these while still being able to manufacture economically. Johnston sought and received help from others who were more expert in the use of particular materials and manufacturing processes – the Okespur company and the Malaysian Rubber Producers Research Association. There was also a need to fit in with the national and international regulations and standards of football associations.

Johnston's story confirms the message from every previous example of innovation, from Edison to Haberman, that determination and perseverance, perhaps obsession, are vital for anyone involved in invention and innovation. But as you saw in Section 2 an individual inventor also needs to be prepared to compromise on the original vision to accommodate the needs of manufacture and marketing. Just as Johnston had to accept a technical compromise between rebound properties and strength, he also had to accept a marketing compromise between design for improved properties and an appearance likely to be acceptable to the market. However, the final compromise, which saw the Predator launched as a luxury boot rather than the cheap coaching aid Johnston had first intended, shows where the balance of power inevitably lies between individual inventors and organisations funding innovation.

4.2.3 Kicking off again

Like many individual inventors Craig Johnston never stops having inventive ideas. He's also devised a sensor system to detect and record when bottles are removed from hotel minibars (the Butler), a globally successful TV game show concept (*The Main Event*) and a software system that analyses a football player's performance to improve their game (Supaskills). But his dissatisfaction at having had to compromise over the Predator clearly niggled at him. In 2003 he patented a slip-on plastic skin for football boots, with rubber spikes to achieve improved grip and control similar to the Predator. He called his invention the Pig because of its ugly appearance and the squealing noises it made when he first tried it out in the wet (Figure 95). At the time of writing (2005) he was still looking for venture capital support but his aim was for the Pig to sell for around £20 so that children could afford it. Johnston was also one of the nominees for the London Design Museum's designer of the year award for 2004.

Figure 95　Craig Johnston holding the Pig boot Source: Reuters

4.3　Inventors within organisations

So far in this section you've seen how lone inventors have exploited their ideas by setting up their own companies or by seeking the help of established organisations. But there are many individuals involved with invention and innovation who are working inside organisations.

Organisations are not anonymous bodies with a life of their own; they consist of individuals and groups or teams working both independently and cooperatively. I'll take a brief look now at the roles that can be played by inventors within organisations. In the more innovation-minded organisations, individuals are given a certain amount of freedom and are encouraged to develop inventive ideas that might turn into successful innovations for the company.

4.3.1 Post-it notes

At the time of the development of the sticky Post-it note the large American-owned corporation 3M set its divisions the goal of deriving a certain percentage of their sales from products introduced in the past 5 years. In addition a staff member could devote 15 per cent of his or her time in independent research to prove that a particular product was feasible and could recruit a team to develop a product idea, with salaries and promotions tied to the product's success. Such an environment encouraged individuals in the company to come up with a variety of novel ideas – one of the most successful being the Post-it adhesive note pad.

Spencer Silver was an employee who, while experimenting with polymer-based adhesives, accidentally came up with a mixture that provided tack between two surfaces but it would not bond tightly to them (Figure 96). It was a curiosity in that it was not a conventional glue and had no obvious application. The organisation couldn't be persuaded that it had potential and Silver's team moved on to other projects. However Silver stuck at his task and persuaded 3M to patent the discovery (Figure 97). The first application he came up with was for a bulletin board that was sticky all over but early prototypes weren't successful.

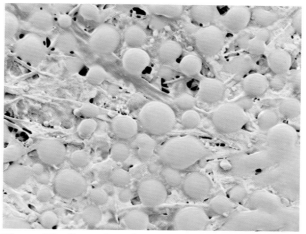

Figure 96 Scanning electron micrograph of the sticky surface of a Post-it
Source: Science Photo Library

The bumps are spheres of urea formaldehyde resin 15–40 micrometres in diameter that rupture easily under finger pressure. Each time the Post-it note's sticky strip is pressed to a surface a few spheres burst and release a film of glue. The stickers can be reused until all of the spheres have burst.

After 5 years Silver was transferred to the commercial tape division under a new boss, Geoff Nicholson, who had a brief and resources to develop new products. What was needed was a problem to match Silver's solution. This was provided by another member of the new team, Arthur Fry. Fry sang in a choir and was frustrated by regularly losing the bits of paper he used as bookmarks in his songbook. After a while Fry had a moment of insight and realised that what was needed was Silver's weak adhesive on the bookmarks. Two more members of the research team, Henry Courtney and Roger Merrill, then came up with a way of making the adhesive stay on the original paper rather than on any surface it was attached to. Then it took a further 2 years

3,691,140

1

ACRYLATE COPOLYMER MICROSPHERES

BACKGROUND OF THE INVENTION

This invention relates to inherently tacky, elastomeric, solvent-dispersible, solvent-insoluble, acrylate copolymer and a process of preparing the copolymer.

Aerosol spray adhesives have recently found commercial importance in the graphic arts for adhering paper to various substrates, as well as numerous other uses. Such adhesives have many desirable properties. For instance, they permit paper to be removed from a substrate to which it is adhered, without tearing; however, they do not permit rebonding. These adhesives generally comprise solvent dispersions of cross-linked rubbers or acrylates. Such polymers, while commercially utilizable, are not completely satisfactory because the cross-linking reaction is difficult to control and often provides soluble or partially soluble polymers. Soluble polymers are undesirable for spray adhesives having a non-volatile content above 10 percent because they do not atomize well and therefore fail to spray or form a "cobweb" spray pattern. Also, such polymers form agglomerates of random size, the large particles often plugging the spray nozzle orifice. Further, the polymer particles, when dry, agglomerate and are dispersible only with difficulty.

Despite the desirability of inherently tacky, elastomeric polymers which are solvent-dispersible, solvent-insoluble, and of uniformly small size, such a product has never heretofore existed.

SUMMARY

The invention provides inherently tacky, elastomeric, polymers which are uniformly solvent-insoluble, solvent-dispersible, of small size, and ideally suited for use in aerosol spray adhesives. The polymers easily disperse in various solvents to provide non-plugging suspensions which spray without cobwebbing. The polymers permit bonding of paper and other materials to various substrates, permit easy removal of bonded paper from the substrate without tearing, and also permit subsequent rebonding of the paper without application of additional adhesive.

The invention comprises infusible, solvent-dispersible, solvent-insoluble, inherently tacky, elastomeric, acrylate copolymer microspheres consisting essentially of about 90 to about 99.5 percent by weight of at least one alkyl acrylate ester and about 10 to about 0.5 percent by weight of at least one monomer selected from the group consisting of substantially oil-insoluble, water-soluble, ionic monomers and maleic anhydride. Preferably, the microspheres comprise about 95 to about 99 percent by weight acrylate monomer and about 5 to about 1 percent by weight ionic monomer, maleic anhydride, or a mixture thereof. The microspheres are prepared by aqueous suspension polymerization utilizing emulsifier in an amount greater than the critical micelle concentration in the absence of externally added protective colloids or the like.

Solvent suspensions of these microspheres may be sprayed by conventional techniques without cobwebbing or may be incorporated in aerosol containers

2

adhesion permitting separation, repositioning and re-bonding of adhered objects. Additionally, these polymers are readily removable from surfaces to which they have been applied, much as rubber cements are removable by mere rubbing. Further, the tacky spheres resist permanent deformation, regaining their spherical shape upon release of pressure. They also exhibit a very low film or tensile strength, less than about 10 psi.

The alkyl acrylate ester monomer portion of the copolymer microspheres may comprise one ester monomer or a mixture of two or more ester monomers. Similarly, the water-soluble, substantially oil-insoluble monomer portion of the copolymer microspheres may comprise maleic anhydride alone, an ionic monomer alone, a mixture of two or more ionic monomers, or a mixture of maleic anhydride with one or more ionic monomers.

The alkyl acrylate ester portion of these microspheres consist of those alkyl acrylate monomers which are oleophilic, water-emulsifiable, of restricted water-solubility, and which, as homopolymers, generally have glass transition temperatures below about −20°C. Alkyl acrylate ester monomers which are suitable for the microspheres of the invention include iso-octyl acrylate, 4-methyl-2-pentyl acrylate, 2-methylbutyl acrylate, sec-butyl acrylate, and the like. Acrylate monomers with glass transition temperatures higher than −20°C. (i.e., tert-butyl acrylate, iso-bornyl acrylate or the like) may be used in conjunction with one of the above described acrylate ester monomers.

The water-soluble ionic monomer portion of these microspheres is comprised of those monomers which are substantially insoluble in oil. By substantially oil-insoluble and water-soluble it is meant that the monomer has a solubility of less than 0.5% by weight, and, a distribution ratio at a given temperature (preferably 50°–65C.), of solubility in the oil phase monomer to solubility in the aqueous phase of less than about 0.005, i.e.,

$$D = \frac{\text{Total concentration in organic layer}}{\text{Total concentration in aqueous layer}}$$

Table I illustrates typical distribution ratios (D) for several water-soluble, substantially oil-insoluble ionic monomers.

TABLE I

Oleophilic Monomer	Temp. °C	Hydrophilic Monomer	D
iso-octyl acrylate	50	1,1-dimethyl-1(2-hydroxypropyl)amine methacrylimide	0.005
do	50	1,1,1-trimethylamine methacrylimide	0.0015
do	65	do	0.003
do	50	N,N-dimethyl-N-(β-methacryloxyethyl) ammonium propionate betaine	<0.002
do	65	do	0.003
do	65	4,4,9-trimethyl-4-azonia-7-oxo-8-oxa-dec-9-ene-1sulfonate	<0.002
do	65	1,1-dimethyl-1(2,3-dihydroxypropyl)amine methacrylimide	0.0015
do	65	sodium acrylate	<0.001

Figure 97 Post-it patent US3691140 Source: van Dulken, 2002

Even in summary form you can see the invention involves complex chemistry

for a team of designers, mechanical engineers and machine operators used to producing rolls of adhesive tape, to develop new machinery that could produce sheets of a product that was not sticky at all on one side, was only sticky on part of the other side and wasn't very sticky anywhere. 3M decided not to patent this new machinery. By not having to reveal the details of how it worked in a patent description the company was able to maintain relative secrecy about the construction and operation of the machinery. This has made it more difficult for other companies to copy the product.

3M's conventional approach to marketing new products at the time was by circulating brochures describing the product and only sending product samples to those who responded to the advertising. However Post-it was such an innovative product that it was difficult for people to imagine how it might be useful. It transpired that the success of the Post-it was dependent on people using the product. Joe Ramey, the general sales manager of 3M's commercial tape division, started to flood some of the 3M offices with the product and even went as far as giving away the product free on the streets of selected cities. Reorders for Post-it came in at the rate of 90 per cent, which was twice that of earlier successful office products. The Post-it note pad was launched in several regions of the USA in 1978 and nationally in 1980.

Following the success of Post-its, 3M developed a range of products based on Silver's discovery, including a successful version of Silver's very first idea – the self-stick bulletin board.

Exercise 3   Post-it innovation process

Having read this condensed account of the development of the Post-it, consider what you think it illustrates about the innovation process. Specifically think about how it illustrates:

1   role of product champions

2   role of chance

3   act of insight for this invention

4   role of improvers

5   role of a prototype in marketing

6   role of individuals when innovation takes place within an organisation.

Spend 30 minutes making notes on the above topics before looking at the discussion below.

Discussion

1   Role of product champions

Even in an innovation-minded company like 3M there was a natural resistance to something brand new by designers, mechanical engineers and machine operators, then by marketing and sales people. The resistance was overcome by the drive and enthusiasm of those supporters of the invention, the product champions Nicholson, Fry and Ramey.

2   Role of chance

There were at least two examples of chance playing a part:

● Silver's polymer discovery

● Fry's bookmark eureka moment.

3   Act of insight for this invention

This invention involved an example of Usher's act of insight and Koestler's bisociation, both of which you encountered in Section 2. Fry associated two unrelated ideas: the need for a bookmark for his songbook and Silver's adhesive. The paper-to-paper insight for a use of Silver's adhesive had not been realised in 5 years by those working close to it – it came to Fry in a flash when he was a relative newcomer to the subject. But chance alone is not enough – innovation requires such chance breakthroughs to be built upon.

4   Role of improvers

The initial invention of Silver's adhesive needed further development by improvers (3M researchers Courtney and Merrill) to achieve the characteristics that were required by Fry's Post-it note idea. A crucial aspect of developing the invention into a commercial innovation was the devising of an appropriate manufacturing process, which in this case involved inventing new machinery.

5   Role of a prototype in marketing

A prototype model or sample is useful for people to be able to appreciate the qualities and potential of an invention they've never seen before. Giving samples of the Post-it to 3M's own employees helped build up support for the market potential of the product.

6 Role of individuals when innovation takes place within an organisation

There existed a corporate culture at 3M that was supportive of innovation and allowed individuals time to explore their own new ideas. Within an organisation there can be a tension between the need for creative individuals to pursue inventive ideas, which is often a random and unordered activity, and the need of the organisation itself for order and predictability. The Post-it story is an example of success stemming from an organisation being prepared to tolerate, and even support to some extent, a certain amount of lone-inventor behaviour. In addition the individual inventor within such an organisation has the huge advantage of access to other people's expertise and to the resources necessary to transform inventive ideas into an innovation. Such individuals have the benefits of both the freedom to pursue their own ideas and the team work necessary to iron out any practical difficulties and bring the ideas to fruition. Not that 3M is necessarily a typical organisation.

4.4 Is there a future for the lone inventor?

There is a perception that society has always tended to treat inventors badly – this is particularly felt by inventors themselves. This is partly because many independent inventors are stubborn and sometimes eccentric characters who often find it difficult to understand the lack of enthusiasm of others for their inventions. It is also partly because established institutions usually prefer predictability and order rather than change and innovation.

In their classic study *The Sources of Invention* Jewkes, Sawers and Stillerman (1969) suggest that, despite the relative decline of the individual inventor in the face of increasing inventive activity in research institutions and large companies, independent inventors can continue to make contributions in the future and should be encouraged by governments to do so. Jewkes argues that, although this institutionalisation of innovation has been in progress for over a century and is now widespread, inventors working independently have been responsible for some of the most significant inventions in the past – the jet engine, xerography, Kodachrome, the hovercraft – and will continue to come up with great ideas. Jewkes et al suggest that three questions can throw light on how much an individual inventor is dependent on the support of an organisation, or is truly a 'lone' inventor.

Question 1 Who chooses the field of ideas in which the inventor works?

Question 2 Who provides the resources for the inventor's work?

Question 3 Who stands to gain directly from the inventions?

In the case of truly lone inventors the inventors themselves choose the field in which to work, provide the necessary resources themselves and gain the rewards. However it is rare for this to happen on anything other than a small scale – almost at the level of craftwork say. Although you've already seen a number of exceptions in the form of Hickman's Workmate, Dyson's Ballbarrow and Haberman's cup, these are exceptions rather than the norm. At the other extreme of inventors working for an organisation, it is the organisation that chooses the field, provides the resources and reaps the benefits, as with the Post-it and the majority of large-scale innovations. In between there are differing degrees of dependence. A common situation is for an individual inventor to choose the field of ideas and provide resources for initial work then for outsiders, sponsors or organisations to provide more resources to help develop the invention into an innovation. Johnston's boot is one example of this process. The question of gain might then be determined in proportion to the relative level of resource invested by the parties – although it is a common complaint of inventors that their own 'gain' is often disproportionately small.

Jewkes et al put forward four reasons to explain the decline in the relative significance of the individual inventor.

1   Individual inventors often do not have enough money to test out their ideas.

2   Individual inventors tend not to have sufficient scientific or technological training to be able to make use of the latest knowledge in their invention.

3   Individual inventors often lack contact with like-minded workers and the stimulus that such contacts can provide.

4   As more research institutions are established, an increasing number of talented individuals are tempted into the greater security of working as part of a team in an organisation, rather than working on their own.

However Jewkes et al also identify four key contributions they believe individual inventors will always bring to the process of invention.

1   *The uncommitted mind.* A fresh approach not constrained by existing thinking and practice can involve fewer inhibitions about challenging accepted ideas and trying out simple solutions when those better informed are searching for results by more complex and scientific routes. (Remember Christensen's point that disruptive innovation often offers a simpler solution compared with existing technology.)

2   *Outlandish exploration.* Individuals can devote themselves to pursuing unorthodox ideas. The chances of success will be reduced but if success is achieved it will be all the larger because greater originality will have been achieved than if the exploration had been more conservative. (The idea of adding rubber fins to a soccer boot was quite outlandish.)

3   *The importance of observation.* Many discoveries and inventions have been the product of an individual's skilled observation and intuitive recognition of the significance of unexpected variations in what is being observed. (Each of the cases in this section had an example of observation leading to a breakthrough.)

4   *The advantages of large numbers.* Given that each new invention opens up further opportunities for invention, and that this constantly expanding universe of ideas, knowledge and techniques cannot be explored exhaustively by research organisations, there will always be some room for individual inventors to make a contribution.

Jewkes and his colleagues conclude that although inventive individuals are increasingly working inside organisations, making it more likely that new inventions will come from such sources, this might be a mixed blessing. They suggest that organisations can restrict the sort of individual creativity vital for invention by placing constraints on behaviour. Further, they argue that independence of thought and action have always been important to invention and that national technology policy ought to be encouraging those individuals who choose to work independently. Finally they point out that individual users of industrial and consumer products are well placed to identify aspects of existing products that need improving, or needs that could be met by the invention of a new product. (This is something you should bear in mind when choosing an idea for your project.)

But if invention is to be more than just an individual's hobby it has to be linked to some kind of entrepreneurial activity. Entrepreneurial activity is as important for innovation as creativity is for invention. Every inventive individual has to become involved with some sort of organisation before the innovation stage can be reached, whether it is inventors selling an invention to a company for exploitation or setting up a company of their own for the purposes of developing the idea into an innovation.

Further, given that modern technology and its products are highly complex and often science-based, the knowledge and resources needed for successful innovation go far beyond those available to a single individual or even a small group. Innovation therefore requires teamwork and some kind of organised effort. Inventors usually need the support of improvers to transform an inventive idea into a prototype capable of being manufactured. Engineering design plays an important role in ensuring the new product is designed to use appropriate materials and manufacturing processes, and industrial design ensures it is easy to use and attractive for potential users. Product champions and entrepreneurs are needed to provide the resources necessary to develop a working prototype into a marketable innovation. However, while entrepreneurs and investors might have commercial skills and an awareness of the market, they need to rely on the inventive and technical ability of inventors and improvers to produce the innovative product in the first place.

But remember the infrastructure that Edison created around himself? It always was necessary to set up an organisation to make and launch an innovation on a profitable scale – that hasn't changed. And teamwork always was important. Before they could transform their inventive ideas into practical working products, great inventors of the past, such as Edison and Bell, needed the support of others – toolmakers, workshop technicians, designers, engineers, lawyers and marketing experts (Figure 98).

Given the need for such a network of support, are individual inventors discouraged from even starting to invent? Apparently not, to judge from the attention given to invention and innovation by TV series – current UK examples include *Best Inventions* and *Innovation Nation*. And there are regular exhibitions of the work of individuals that aim to bring together inventors and innovative companies with investors, private and corporate manufacturers and business people. One such exhibition I attended displayed the work of more than 250 individual inventors. Ideas ranged from the simple to the sophisticated. A simple

Figure 98   Edison and some of the team working with him in his laboratory in Orange, New Jersey, on improvements to the phonograph in 1888 Source: Edison National Historic Site

invention was an instantly inflatable 'car passenger' to promote feelings of driver safety – whereas a sophisticated invention was a robotic aid for the severely disabled, controlled by the blink of an eye. There were light-hearted inventions, such as a manufacturing process to produce water-skimming stones of a standard size and weight. And there were serious ones such as a composition that can fireproof plastics and foam if added at the manufacturing stage or act as a fire-retardant coating for existing plastics products. There were inventions designed to meet well-established needs, such as a device to raise and hold a door in position, enabling a single individual to hang a door. And there were some offering things you didn't know you needed, such as a vacuum cleaner in the form of a video cassette to clean the interior of a VCR. It seemed clear that there was still a wealth of individual inventiveness. Indeed there was an electric atmosphere at the exhibition as inventors searched the crowds for potential investors and those with the resources looked for a potential winner among the exhibits.

Increased scientific and technological complexity doesn't seem to have stopped inventive activity among the population. Each generation throws up its own inventive heroes like James Dyson (Figure 99) and Trevor Baylis (Figure 100). Maybe the 'big' innovations are more likely to originate within companies than in the past but there doesn't seem to be any stopping creative individuals from coming up with ideas for new and improved products and trying to get them onto the market.

SAQ 11

Recall what Section 3 said about overcoming obstacles to innovation. What were the main technical, financial and organisational obstacles facing Craig Johnston's improved soccer boot? How were these obstacles overcome?

SAQ 12

Can individuals working in teams in large organisations be creative or do organisations tend to restrict individual creativity?

SAQ 13

Is it inevitable that government or large commercial organisations will always be the key players in developing and financing innovation?

Figure 99   James Dyson and his cyclonic vacuum cleaner
Source: Rex Features

Figure 100   Trevor Baylis with a collection of his wind-up clockwork radios
Source: Rex Features

Key points of Section 4

- Using a product can lead to ideas for its improvement.

- An individual inventor with no prior specialist knowledge, other than as a user of existing products, can take an inventive idea towards innovation but this can be costly.

- Innovation carries a big financial risk for individuals but if they are prepared to take the risk and can prove there's a market for their product then commercial companies might give resources.

- Individual inventors tend not to have sufficient scientific or technological training to be able to make use of the latest knowledge in their invention, so they need to seek specialist help.

- Individuals should be careful in their dealings with commercial organisations. The resolution of any dispute often comes down to financial muscle and nerve.

- Individuals need to be determined and persistent. But an inventor also needs to be prepared to compromise to accommodate the needs of manufacture and marketing.

- It is less costly and risky for an individual inventor to have their idea taken up by a company already working in that field. Though there is often resistance to a new product from outside that challenges a firm's existing products ('not invented here').

- Even in innovation-minded companies, people's natural resistance to something new has to be overcome by the enthusiasm of the product champions.

- A crucial aspect of developing an invention into a commercial innovation is the work of improvers in designing the product for efficient manufacture, reliability, safety, appearance and ease of use.

- A prototype model is useful for people to be able to appreciate the qualities and potential of an invention they've never seen before.

- The chances of successful innovation for an organisation increase if it is prepared to tolerate, and even support, a certain amount of lone-inventor behaviour from some of its employees.

- Individual inventors will always be able to contribute an uncommitted mind prepared to challenge existing ideas; outlandish exploration of unorthodox ideas; skilled observation and intuitive recognition of the significance of what is observed.

- Given that modern technology and its products are highly complex, the knowledge and resources needed for innovation go far beyond those available to an individual. Innovation therefore requires teamwork and organised effort.

- Innovations are more likely to originate within companies than in the past, but there doesn't seem to be any stopping creative individuals from coming up with inventions and trying to get them onto the market.

The key points for Section 4 meet learning outcomes 1.1, 1.3, 1.4, 1.12, 1.13, 1.14, 2.1 and 2.2.

5 Impact of new technologies

The following quote from a UK government department highlights some of the new technologies that are expected to have an impact.

> ... technology and scientific understanding are changing our world faster than ever before. Developments in information and communications technologies (ICT), new materials, biotechnology, new fuels and nanotechnology are unleashing new waves of innovation, and creating many opportunities for entrepreneurial businesses to gain competitive advantage;

(Department of Trade and Industry, 2003, p. 8)

At the end of Section 3 I asked what were the implications of accelerating change and growing technological complexity in the twenty-first century. In Section 4 I concluded that there seems to be a continuing role for the individual inventor, despite the growing complexity of technology and the need for increasingly specialised knowledge and skills. I will now look at the impact of new technologies, particularly those based on advances in scientific knowledge, such as ICT and nanotechnology. Further, I'll consider the effect of these new technologies on the way society is organised and at some of the concerns about the impact of innovation on the environment.

Successive waves of technological innovation have had a significant impact on the way society has organised itself and has done business. Growing centralisation and urbanisation together with the rise of the corporation set the initial pattern for industrialised society. Then electric power was supplied overland by cable, which permitted the spread of industrialisation. Electricity also was the means for communicating over long distances, initially with coded messages and then with the telephone and radio. Advances in chemistry resulted in previously unknown synthetic materials of many kinds, from dyes to plastics, fibres to vinyls. This led to an increase in the number and variety of goods available to buy – which, along with growing prosperity, helped establish the consumer society. Electronics increased the volume and distance of communication and extended people's outlook from parochial to international. The combination of microelectronics, computing and communications technology has allowed multinational corporations to grow and thrive and globalised products to emerge. As well as providing us with a range of new products, information and communication technologies (ICT) have become a dominant influence on the way the world is run. The emergence of ICT as a group of interrelated technologies means economic and technological activity has changed so radically that some argue ICT has created a new techno-economic regime.

5.1 Impact of information and communication technologies

5.1.1 Characteristics of information and communication technologies

There are four aspects of innovation that underlie ICT and that account for its impact.

1 *Change from mechanics to electronics.* There has been a change from mechanical and electromechanical systems to electronics. Increasingly technology with moving parts has been replaced by solid-state components. So the telephone that used to have a rotating dial now has push buttons that generate tones. These changes usually mean a reduction in the number of separate parts needed and an increase in reliability because components are not subject to mechanical wear and are less susceptible to breakage.

2 *Miniaturisation.* One of the most amazing changes is the reduction in size of devices that conduct electricity or switch electrical signals. The invention of the transistor in 1947, the integrated circuit in 1959 and the microprocessor in 1971 all permitted a big jump in computing power accompanied by a reduction in size (Figures 101 and 102). Associated improvements in manufacturing technology were vital in helping to achieve this miniaturisation. The process of increasing power and functionality and reducing size and cost seems to be continuous.

You may have come across Moore's Law – a famous prediction made in 1965 by Gordon Moore, cofounder of the microelectronics firm Intel (Moore, 1965). According to this prediction the number of circuits etched on a given piece of silicon could double every year. In 1975 he changed the timescale to two years but it has since entered computer folklore as 18 months. At this rate personal computers could become a hundred times more powerful every decade. So far this is one of the few predictions in the area of computing that is turning out to be accurate. The first electronic computer in 1946 contained 18 000 valves, weighed 30 tonnes and occupied an area of 160 m^2. The first single-chip microprocessor in 1971 contained 2300 transistors and was the size of a thumb. Today (2005) the standard computer on which I'm typing this is based on a microprocessor containing 55 million transistors (Figure 102).

3 *Digitalisation.* With information represented as the binary digits of 0 and 1 and microprocessors able to read this information in less than a millionth of a second, the switch from analogue to digital has improved the speed and accuracy of many technologies. Another key factor is the suitability of digital data to be transmitted and reassembled accurately at its destination.

4 *Software.* With ICT change can often consist of rewriting lines of code in a computer program rather than the redesign and construction of devices and machines. This means that more frequent incremental changes are possible and economical. Furthermore it's easier to customise the technology to the needs of the user.

Figure 101 ENIAC digital calculator at Los Alamos National Laboratory, USA
Source: Science Photo Library

Early computers did not have the benefit of miniaturisation permitted by integrated circuits. The first electronic computer, the electronic numerical integrator and calculator (ENIAC) was completed in 1946 by two American scientists from the University of Pennsylvania, John W. Mauchly and J. Presper Eckert, working under contract to the Ballistic Research Laboratory. Its first use was to calculate ballistic trajectories.

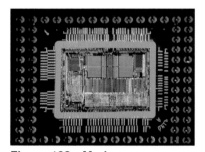

Figure 102 Modern microprocessor chip Source: Science Photo Library

Microprocessors have been incorporated into ever more products – initially it was to give them 'intelligence' to enable them to be programmed and controlled. The next stage was to get appliances to exchange information and respond accordingly. And now the old distinctions in communication products are breaking down. The telephone is no longer thought of as being only for voice communication because mobile phones can transmit pictures, video, music, data and can connect to the internet (Figure 103). Computers can receive and send information, can download and play music and video and can make transactions. This has led to a multiplicity of ICT

Figure 103 A mobile phone and a wireless computer can be used almost anywhere Source: courtesy of Vismedia and BT

Public wireless networks called BT Openzones were installed in Costa coffee shops in 2004 as part of a nationwide rollout of wireless networks

(a)

(b)

Figure 104   Examples of ICT products: (a) digital camera; (b) MP3 player Sources: (a) Fujifilm (b) Sony

products that are increasingly interlinked with each other through wireless networks.

A recent survey of UK computer users – who are likely to be 'innovators' or early adopters – showed the following ownership levels for ICT products (Figure 104):

mobile phone 93%

desktop PC 77%

interactive TV 49%

digital camera 44%

laptop PC 29%

mobile internet connection 27%

home broadband connection 25%

MP3 player 18%

bluetooth enabled device 12%

wireless enabled laptop 9%, but 18% would like it

mobile phone with camera 9%

have used wireless hotspot 7%, but 50% are not interested

3G mobile phone 4%.

(data source: ICM Research, published in Internet Magazine, 2004)

By the time you read this the pattern of use will be different. One of the key innovations that underpins much of the networking of ICT products is the internet and its most visible application is the World Wide Web.

5.1.2 ICT, the internet and the Web

As you probably know the internet is a global network of computer networks. It developed from US military research in the 1950s and 1960s into how to set up a decentralised network of computers that could maintain communications in the face of a nuclear attack. Against a background of continuous improvements to the performance of computers outlined above, the idea of the internet was made workable by a series of inventions by scientific researchers. Initially this allowed a number of users to access a computer at the same time and, once communications standards had been agreed, enabled different types of computer to exchange information at a distance.

A key aspect of its breakout into the mainstream was the culture of the computer science research community in which it was developed. The source code that lay at the heart of internet software was cooperatively written, freely shared and always regarded as being in the public domain. Aided by the invention of email and conferencing systems that encouraged rapid and widespread exchange of ideas, source code was therefore worked on by a large number of creative minds. Unlike the simultaneous invention in the past the early development of the internet was not taking place in an environment of commercial competition, although there was much intellectual competition.

Motivation was individual technical curiosity, satisfaction at solving problems and a desire to achieve a reputation with the rest of the technical community. This cooperative simultaneous invention, in which software improvements were shared with others and freely incorporated into improved versions of the product, contributed to the increasing pace of development.

When commercial companies started to try to profit from licensing their software there was a reaction among the research community. The Free Software Foundation was set up to protect the right to access source code, alter it and share changes with others – a principle it called copyleft. So the creation of adaptable, versatile software and the collaborative, enthusiastic approach of a growing community of technologists combined to help the internet develop from relatively specialised research use into a medium for mass communication. Although there is now much commercialisation of the internet, the cooperative culture that gave birth to the internet continues to sustain its development. This has seen the operating system Linux being developed since the early 1990s to the extent that it has now captured a quarter of the market for internet servers – although Microsoft's Windows system is used on the majority of personal computers.

However to some extent the physical structure of the internet and its culture are still the province of computer enthusiasts (techies). For the average computer user the public manifestation of the internet is the Web. The Web was invented in 1989 by English physicist Tim Berners-Lee (Figure 105) working at CERN, the European particle physics laboratory in Geneva. Given the number of disparate people working at the lab, the rapid turnover of personnel and the increasing complexity of information they needed to access, Berners-Lee set about designing a searchable linked-information system. He decided to base it on hypertext, a non-sequential information structure that allowed any user to follow origins and links of material across boundaries of documents, servers, networks, and individual implementations.

Figure 105   Tim Berners-Lee (born 1955), English computer scientist and principal inventor of the World Wide Web, photographed in 1995 Source: Science Photo Library

The Web went public in January 1991 with the original text-based browser and use of the new network grew steadily. However in 1993 a second wave of innovation was launched with the release of a graphical browser called Mosaic that allowed web pages to include images for the first time. At first Berners-Lee was critical of what he saw as a frivolous addition, telling Mosaic's inventor 'this was supposed to be a serious medium – this is serious information'. (Remember Edison and his views on the use of the phonograph.) However, as with email and conferencing on the internet, it was the addition of images that turned the Web into a mass medium – in fact the World Wide Web.

In 2 years the volume of traffic on the internet involving web pages went from almost nothing to nearly a quarter of the total. The growth of the Web was like the process by which previous communications technologies had spread – but with one vital difference. Whereas the spread of the telephone depended on massive investment in physical infrastructure the Web simply built on the internet's existing infrastructure. In the early days of the telephone, for example, people were reluctant to use the new technology because there were so few other people with telephones that it was hardly worth the effort. The same was true for email. But the Web achieved a critical mass of users so quickly that it broke through many of the usual barriers to diffusion.

The statistics for internet use are staggering, both in terms of the numbers of users who are estimated to access it, and its rate of growth. NUA is an organisation that maintains up-to-date internet trends and statistics based on an analysis of survey data. This includes a 'How Many Online?' section that estimates how many people use the internet worldwide (Figure 106). As of September 2002 the number was 605 million, about 10 per cent of the world's population. (Data source: NUA.com, 2005). In the UK, internet use grew from 500 000 users in 1995 to more than 20 million in 2003. (Data source: Continental Research, published in Internet Magazine, 2003.) You can check the latest figures yourself on the internet.

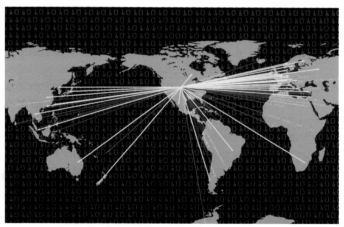

Figure 106 Internet traffic volume can be measured and represented
Source: Science Photo Library

To describe the internet as a global network of computer networks is true up to a point, but it misses out what is perhaps the most significant part of the system, namely the people who use it. The internet is a great technological achievement. But it is also a powerful social system and an example of the way in which a dominant technology can affect the way in which society organises itself. It enables people to communicate and interact in ways that were never hitherto possible. It is also the first relatively uncensored communications medium in history. And because it is an open-access system, anyone can join in provided they have access to some basic equipment and a communications link. However, as you saw in Section 3 on the diffusion of MP3 audio, there have been some attempts to control the internet by commercial companies who feel their interests are threatened.

As well as being an innovation in itself the internet can also encourage the development of innovation. It can provide inventors with access to a huge amount of information, to new ideas and to a community of other creative individuals. The internet has also introduced new ways of doing business (Figure 107). It costs considerably less to create a presence on the Web for a business than it does to create a physical presence such as buying and fitting out a shop. And once on the Web a company can reach a significantly larger customer base than by traditional means. On the one hand the internet encourages small, independent companies to flourish, yet at the same time it increases the power and market position of the dominant companies. As you will know from using search engines, trying to find anything on the Web can be frustrating. So people tend to go straight to names they know, and because they are well-known brands they trust them also.

Figure 107   The computer screen substitutes for the shop window and sales counter

But the internet is also an example of a disruptive innovation in terms of the impact it can have on existing social and business structures. Many companies exist in their current form due to a combination of geographical convenience and economic sense – it is easier for customers if everything is in one place and the costs of the various components make it more advantageous to bundle them together.

The internet challenges some of these reasons. The internet can make each element of an organisation vulnerable. Someone offering just one particular function online may be able to offer it cheaper or better. So this can lead to the dismantling and reformulation of traditional business structures, involving what some commentators have called disintermediation. This term sounds rather alarming but involves processes that are familiar. One aspect is where the ultimate producer of a product or service bypasses existing intermediaries and sells directly to the consumer. For example the internet makes it feasible for a car manufacturer to sell direct to the public. Before the internet it was difficult for a customer to buy a car in this way because only recognised dealers were allowed to buy from the manufacturer. This made economic sense for the manufacturer that could not deal directly with thousands, maybe millions of customers, so it was a better model to spread the sales load through dealers. But it didn't make as much sense for the customer as this meant that the dealer's profit was added to the cost of buying a car.

However ICT and the increase in connectivity means that consumers can now buy direct from a manufacturer's website, choosing a model and specification, without interacting with sales staff. These orders can be placed directly and the availability of cars made known to the customer, again through the internet without the need for a salesperson. This does not mean all car dealerships will disappear or that changes will happen overnight – people have the habit of buying a car in a certain way – but there's no doubt it has stirred up the existing system. At least it has increased pressure on car retailers in the UK to drop their prices or add extra value to deals on new cars. In the long term the changes may be more dramatic.

The second way the internet can lead to disintermediation is where a new intermediary emerges, employing a lower-cost way of distributing the product or service and challenging existing intermediaries. To continue with the car-buying example JamJar Cars is an internet-based car retailer that has emerged to challenge traditional car dealers. Launched in 2000, by 2004 it was claiming to be the UK's leading car retailer. Once again, even if this claim is exaggerated, such a new business has had a disruptive influence on the established market.

5.1.3 ICT and the manufacturing process

You saw in Section 3 that the manufacturing process itself has been the subject of much innovation. The introduction of computers, satellite communication and the internet has had a significant effect on the development and production of new products. Computer-aided design and simulation has revolutionised engineering and other professional practices. In addition the internet makes it possible for people in different locations to collaborate on the same design.

Computer-aided manufacturing and robotics are beginning to transform the production floor. The planning and synchronisation of production can be organised over great distances, bringing together for assembly components produced in different locations.

In the twentieth century multinational corporations appeared, meaning corporations that owned more or less independent facilities in several countries. Then there were transnational corporations where the cooperation between the different locations of such a company transcended national boundaries. Now we have global corporations where ICT has permitted globally planned and coordinated activities.

Machines dedicated to one type of operation make commercial sense only in a situation of high-volume production of an unchanging product design. To change the design would require expensive alteration of the machine settings. But as the trend towards high-value, low-volume manufacture gathered pace, a more flexible method of manufacture was needed to enable companies to deliver customised products to target markets.

Developments in computer-aided design (CAD) permitted a new product to be completely specified before manufacture and then the parameters of the design to be converted into instructions for numerically controlled machine tools to carry out machining of components. This came to be called computer-aided manufacture (CAM) and when CAD is closely tied to CAM an integrated process called CADCAM ensues.

Such technological innovations, with their ease of modelling changes, also encouraged the development of more efficient designs and cheaper manufacturing processes that used fewer parts and materials.

A further step towards the complete automation of production was taken with the introduction of computer-controlled handling and inspection machinery – for example automated materials handling systems connected to groups of workstations. Robots were first used in industry in the mid-1970s, though the first patent application on a programmable robot was made in 1954 in the USA. Robots were used in harsh environments such as paint spraying and welding, largely by automobile manufacturers (Figure 108). Another advance in the automation of production was the use of the automatic guided vehicle (AGV). Such vehicles were first used in a commercial operation in the FIAT body plant in 1979 where they were used to move body shells between different robot welding stations. Their strength lay in their flexibility to be programmed for different sequences of movements rather than repeating a standard pattern as was common in mass production. They were also the key to new systems of computerised warehousing, packing and dispatch.

Figure 108　Robots welding on a car assembly line Source: Science Photo Library

Once computer control spread to business systems it became possible to control all aspects of the manufacturing process, from market predictions, through design and manufacture, to dispatch to the customer. Computer integrated manufacturing (CIM) uses computers to deal with every aspect of production: forecasting the demand for the finished product; processing customer orders; generating the engineering data needed for production; calculating the overall production schedule; ordering and storing components from suppliers; stock control; materials handling and delivery to the appropriate place and time in the production system; managing the manufacturing activity to minimise work in progress; monitoring the production process including coordinating inspection; and compiling cost information on the entire process for accounting purposes.

In a commercial environment where change is often difficult to predict the emphasis is on increasing the speed and flexibility of the manufacturing process even further – a move towards what is called agile manufacturing. There are a number of reasons behind this trend.

- Global competition is intensifying.

- Mass markets are fragmenting into niche markets with more products tailored to the needs of specific customers.

- Customers are coming to expect low-volume, high-quality, customised products.

- Customers increasingly want to be treated as individuals and to have a say in the design of the products they buy – or at least the chance to choose which features they want.

- Cooperation among companies is becoming necessary, including companies who are in direct competition with each other.

- Very short product life cycles, development time and production lead times are required.

The skills and techniques that worked for mass-production do not necessarily apply to products where the customers require small quantities of highly customised, build-to-order (BTO) products. In addition the ability to offer value-added benefits like product upgrades and future reconfigurations can be as important as producing the initial innovative product itself. Leading the BTO movement are the consumer electronics and the automobile industries that have introduced a number of specific approaches to solve some of these problems. Rapid prototyping and rapid tooling provide fast prototype components and tools from three-dimensional CAD data. They are adding to the flexibility and speed of the manufacturing process. Also the use of what is sometimes called a Lego-block approach enables basic assembly of some products to take place with customisation being added only at the final stage.

Of course it's all very well to improve the speed and efficiency of the actual production process but if there are inefficiencies in the rest of the system that takes a customer's order and translates it into a customised product then manufacturing improvements are in vain.

Take the case of automobile manufacture. The proportion of new BTO vehicles in the UK volume car market reached 33 per cent by 2000 but the majority of new vehicles were still sold by the stock-push approach. However many manufacturers are committed to moving in a BTO direction, driven by the prospect of saving money on unwanted stock. Currently (2005) it takes, on average, around 40 days to deliver a car to a customer's specification but only 1.5 days of that time are spent building the vehicle. Following the communication of an order between dealer and manufacturer (3.8 days), most of the time is spent in ordering materials and components from suppliers (9.8 days), organising the scheduling of orders for the factory (14.1 days) and sequencing the assembly process (6 days). Following assembly it takes just under a day to load the vehicle at the factory and almost 4 days to distribute the finished product to the dealer. Current best practice is said to be capable of reducing this 40-day average to less than 13 days, but some major manufacturers have a goal of achieving the '3-day car'. (Source of data: Howard, 2002)

One of the keys to reducing the length of the BTO time is the nature of communications between the various participants in the system. Since 1985 manufacturers – starting in the electronics industry – had used electronic data interchange (EDI) to convert from paperwork to computer-to-computer transfer of information. Purchase orders and invoices could be exchanged with suppliers over an electronic network and even payment could be included in this electronic system. The benefits of EDI included speed (same-day exchange of documents), accuracy (fewer mistakes due to typing or transcription errors) and economy (fewer clerks needed in the purchasing and goods-receiving chain). However there were disadvantages that prevented widespread take-up.

● *Expense*. Most company computing at the time was done by mainframes and the cost of integrating EDI applications was inhibiting.

● *Networking complexity*. EDI required companies to develop extensive and expensive private networks to transmit and receive information to and from a wide variety of customers or suppliers.

● *Emergence of alternatives*. To gain some of the speed advantages of EDI without incurring the expense of computer hardware, software and networks, competitive services emerged (like overnight courier services, facsimile machines) that provided more economical ways of communicating for all but the largest companies.

The arrival of the internet – and in particular the Web – has led to a massive revival of interest in EDI because it removes the need to invest in special computer and networking technology. As virtually every major business now has a website and an internet connection, transferring electronic documents from one company to another with reasonable security has become simple, routine in fact. The cost-savings in online procurement can be considerable. Just to take one example, British Telecom reported that buying goods and services online reduces the cost of processing a transaction by 90 per cent. And the world's leading automobile manufacturers now insist that all their suppliers deal with them through the Web.

But having mentioned the benefit of being able to use the internet, imagine the problems that might be caused for Ford or General Motors by the internet slowing down when general traffic becomes heavy or suffering from the attentions of hackers. So those two companies, along with Chrysler, set up the automotive network exchange (ANX).

ANX is an extranet – it's like a walled-off area of the internet that uses all the techniques of the internet but that is limited to authorised users. Some of these extranet users are inside a particular company while others will be trusted outsiders – clients, consultants, customers, suppliers. Specialist internet service providers are required to deliver agreed standards of speed, reliability and security. Having a dedicated network that is fast and secure allows the automotive companies to do many different tasks such as placing orders, arranging just-in-time delivery, billing, payments, and so on.

Perhaps more interesting is the capability of using shared applications. The automotive industry is a design-intensive industry, from the design of each individual component to the design of an overall car. ANX potentially allows designers to use CAD software over the network (Figure 109). This means designers in different countries could be working simultaneously on the same part. This is only really possible with the improved speed of ANX compared with the internet because CAD can be demanding on network facilities and capacity. Other possibilities include the implementation of groupware, which is software designed to allow a distributed team of people to communicate and work on shared documents.

ANX is now being promoted as the business-class internet and it is predicted to move beyond its application in just the automotive industry and become a standard for all industrial extranets. In turn agile manufacturing, with its aim to keep production steady and predictable and minimise cost and waste in a rapidly changing business environment, is said to be the blueprint for future manufacturing processes.

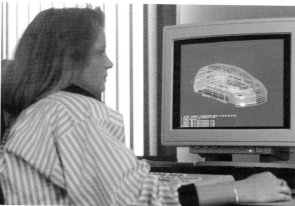

Figure 109　Designer using a computer-aided design workstation
Source: Science Photo Library

5.1.4　Social impact of ICT

We are said to be moving further from the manufacturing focus of the recent past to the service focus of the ICT revolution based on process innovation and control of information rather than the physical manufacture of products. Indeed information can be seen as the latest commodity that is being manipulated by the new computing and communications technologies. But to what extent is the character of work and social life changing in the face of this ICT revolution?

One of the fundamental ideas behind mechanisation of manufacture in the past was to remove the sort of variation introduced when human beings do something. Engineering drawings were introduced so that craftspeople worked to the same design. Machine tools and fine measuring devices were invented to make sure products were reproduced accurately and to standard specifications. Components were standardised and made interchangeable, so that a product could be repaired simply by replacing a failed component. Jobs that required a high level of skill on the part of a worker were broken down into individual actions that could be performed repetitively by less skilled workers. Much of the skill of making something was transferred from people to machines. This was not the result of some sinister plot but was rather an attempt to make new products more efficiently, economically and in greater volume. But the changes in approach introduced by new technologies did affect the people doing the work.

Even though the increasing use of ICT has shifted the focus towards service industries some of the above processes are still at work. In her book *The Making of a Cybertariat: Virtual Work in a Real World* Ursula Huws (2003) discusses how ICT is being used to standardise and strip creativity out of work processes. Extreme current (2005) examples include Chinese women employed to enter data for credit card companies. The work is fragmented so that one set of workers key in postcodes, another surnames, and so on. In India computer operators process medical transcriptions for US doctors. They earn one-eighth of the salary of their US counterparts but four times the salary of an Indian schoolteacher. Some supermarket security cameras in California are monitored by cheap labour in Georgia. In the UK increasing numbers of call centres and technical helpdesks are being outsourced to India thanks to the efficiency of communications. Huws sees us becoming entangled in an ever-growing network of interconnected manufacturing and service relationships run by people with incomplete knowledge of what they're doing and different motivations for doing it.

Communications have become one of the types of infrastructure that tie society together and make possible transactions and exchanges between people. But, says Huws,

> Communication used to be people talking to each other. Then it became writing, and then various electrical and electronic ways of transmitting, like the telegraph and telephone. Entertainment used to be somebody singing; the service industry grew minstrels and then orchestras, then technologies for recording music, which become the basis for mass commodities like the CD or pop music videos.

(quoted in Evans-Pughe, 2003)

Huws thinks people are using technology to turn their working and social lives into commodities. A particular example of this commoditisation is the mobile phone:

We now walk down the road with friends while talking on our mobiles to other people. We're prioritising the distant person over the near one, which is exactly what the phone companies want us to do because it doesn't cost anything to talk to the person you're standing next to.

(quoted in Evans-Pughe, 2003)

It has been argued that the revolutionary developments in ICT are pushing Western industrialised countries at least, into a post-industrial society. This is a society where knowledge is a key commodity, information handling, processing and control are key activities, and where innovation is based less often on inventive individuals having bright ideas and increasingly on teams of people making scientific discoveries or pushing back the boundaries of theoretical knowledge. The innovation process in this post-industrial society is further characterised by an increase in the diversity of new products and the rapidity of their obsolescence. To some extent this has been made possible by technologies such as agile manufacturing that, at the start of the twenty-first century, have enabled the rapidly changing needs of a complex market to be met by more flexible and easily adaptable manufacturing processes. In addition to its increasing volume, technological innovation is seen by some as leading to a change in the nature of human interaction, permitting more decentralisation of activities and communication between vast networks of people and the increasing importance of human services as a wealth-creating activity.

Finally there is some dispute as to whether we are experiencing an incremental increase in the rate of industrialisation or a transition into a radical new post-industrial society. It is difficult to be certain when you and I are still in the middle of many of the changes. You saw in Section 1 how it was difficult to be precise about certain definitions of terms, such as when a creative idea becomes an invention, or whether an innovation is incremental or radical. Likewise opinions differ as to whether a cluster of radical innovations constitutes a new techno-economic regime or technological revolution. Whatever the number of so-called revolutions in the past the long-term historical view would seem to suggest the overall process is evolutionary.

Other than examples given, have you experienced ICT making a social impact?

There's an argument that TV and radio broadcasting capitalist values and lifestyles contributed to the fall of the communist regimes in eastern Europe.

5.2 Appliance of science – nanotechnology

In addition to the impact of ICT, developments in areas such as new materials, biotechnology, new fuels and nanotechnology are leading to new waves of innovation. These increasingly rely on breakthroughs in theoretical knowledge and scientific understanding.

The previous section discussed the miniaturisation used in technology, such as the ever-increasing capacity of microprocessors. Putting millions of transistors on a microprocessor involves measurements in micrometres (one thousandth of a millimetre). But nanotechnology is based on scaling down existing technologies to the next level of miniaturisation, manipulating matter at the atomic scale, measured in nanometres (one thousandth of a micrometre). A nanometre is only a few atoms wide – 40 000 times smaller than the width of an average human hair.

> Nanotechnology is, broadly speaking, the art and science of manipulating and rearranging individual atoms and molecules to create useful materials, devices, and systems.
>
> (Uldrich and Newberry, 2003, p. 22)

When the concept of nanotechnology began to be researched in the 1970s the idea was that it would lead to the building of machines a few nanometres wide – motors, robots and even whole computers far smaller than a cell (Figure 110). This was labelled molecular nanotechnology. This is still the hope of technological optimists but in the meantime some real progress has been made in using nanotechnology to alter the properties of materials – a technique labelled structural nanotechnology.

Figure 110   The fine scale of what can be achieved currently with nanotechnology is illustrated in this electron micrograph of components seen next to a fly's leg Source: Science Photo Library

> Many materials, once they are individually reduced below 100 nanometres, begin displaying a set of unique characteristics based on quantum mechanical forces that are exhibited at that level. Due to these quantum mechanical effects, materials may become more conducting, be able to transfer heat better, or have modified mechanical properties.
>
> (Uldrich and Newberry, 2003, p. 23)

Such new properties are sometimes achieved by manipulating a single material but more often it means mixing different constituent materials in precise, minuscule amounts – at a nanoscale level. The resulting materials often display properties superior to any of their individual constituents in areas such as strength, stiffness, thermal stability, optical clarity, reduced permeability, flame resistance and electrical conductivity. Approximately $2 billion a year is being invested in nanotechnology worldwide in industries such as textiles, plastics and pharmaceuticals. It's true that most nanotechnology companies are still investing more in research and development than they are collecting in revenue but many commercial applications are in advanced stages of development or already on sale.

5.2.1 Nanomaterials – from sun cream to vehicles

You've already seen some current examples – the 'smart' materials mentioned in Section 2. I'll look at a few more examples now and make some guesses at how much these novel applications might be disruptive for established companies.

> [Nanotechnology] has already established a beachhead in the economy. The clothing industry is starting to feel the effects of nanotech. Eddie Bauer, for example, is currently using embedded nanoparticles to create stain-repellent khakis. This seemingly simple innovation will impact not only khaki-wearers, but dry cleaners, who will find their business declining; detergent makers, who will find less of their product moving off the shelf; and stain-removal makers, who will experience a sharp decrease in customers. This modest, fairly low-tech application of nanotechnology is just the small tip of a vast iceberg – an iceberg that threatens to sink even the 'unsinkable' companies.
>
> (Uldrich and Newberry, 2003, p. 15)

Consumer goods

As the quote mentions, the coating of individual fibres of cloth with nanoparticles has produced stain resistance in clothing. Liquid merely beads on the surface of such cloth rather than soaking in. This process has been applied to products sold by a number of clothing companies such as Eddie Bauer, Dockers and Gap.

Nanoclays have improved the performance characteristics of plastics used in beer and soda bottles. These new plastics are increasingly being used for applications previously dominated by other materials such as glass and metal. Reduced weight lowers transportation costs and increased ability to hold pressure extends the shelf life.

Kodak is producing colour screens made of nanostructured polymer films. In combination with organic light emitting diodes (OLEDs) this enables thinner, lighter, more flexible, less power-consuming displays for use in car stereos, cell phones, cameras, PDAs, laptops and televisions (Figure 111).

Vehicles

Some nanomaterials are already being used on an industrial scale. For example carbon nanotubes are embedded in automobile body parts to make the surface electrically conducting. This attracts paint particles more efficiently during the application of paint and eliminates the need for a primer coat.

In 2001 Toyota started using plastic nanocomposites in a vehicle bumper, making it 60 per cent lighter and twice as resistant to denting and scratching. It seems likely that such materials will be used increasingly in other vehicle components, making manufacture more

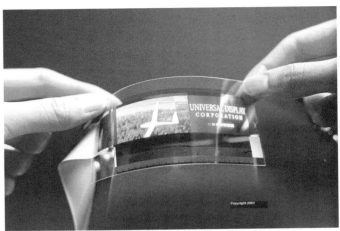

Figure 111   Flexible, organic-light-emitting-diode display Source: courtesy of Universal Display Corporation

efficient, reducing weight and wear and improving strength and durability (Figure 112).

Medical

Cosmetics have been developed using nanoparticulate iron and zinc oxide that is good at absorbing ultraviolet light. Due to the size of the particles they spread more easily, cover better and are transparent. These properties have been exploited in sunscreens, lipstick, moisturisers and numerous ointments. Sunscreens using this nanotechnology were so successful that by 2001 they had captured 60 per cent of the Australian sunscreen market.

A company called AgstroMedica has created a patented material that is close in structure and composition to natural bone by manipulating calcium and phosphate at the molecular level. This novel synthetic bone can be used in areas where natural bone is damaged or has to be removed.

Nanoscale filters have been developed that can filter the smallest of particles, including biological agents and even viruses. This has a range of applications including making it possible to sterilise even the most contaminated water to make it drinkable.

Figure 112   Pencil tip resting on the surface of a micro-accelerator from a car airbag Source: Science Photo Library

The square, mauve pressure sensor detects the rapid deceleration that occurs in a crash. It triggers a circuit that starts the rapid inflation of the bag.

It has been suggested that nanoscale machines with tiny gears such as those in Figure 113 will be small enough to travel inside the human body. It is foreseen that they will deliver drugs to specific sites, or destroy tumour cells or invading bacteria.

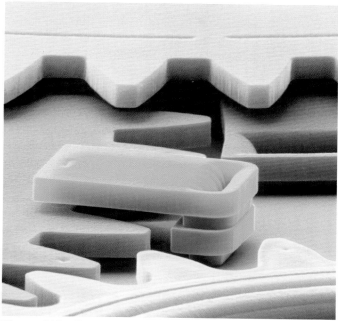

Figure 113   Electron micrograph of nanogears Source: Science Photo Library

Computers

Companies including IBM, Hewlett-Packard, Samsung and NEC are researching the use of carbon nanotubes in non-volatile random-access memory (NRAM). This involves processors that won't forget how to run programs when the power is switched off, enabling instant-on computers. Furthermore chips with NRAM will store many times more data than a silicon chip the same size while the improved conductivity of carbon nanotubes means they can operate faster and with less heat.

The nanowire shown in Figure 114 is just 10 atoms wide. This wire could be used in a computer operating at the limits of miniaturisation. The photonic lattice in Figure 115 is a regular array of rods that was created at Sandia National Labs, USA. Light trapped inside the lattice

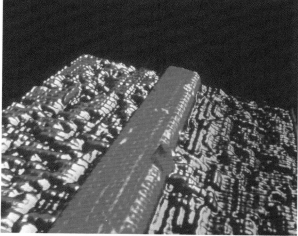

Figure 114   Nanowire made by Hewlett-Packard Source: Science Photo Library

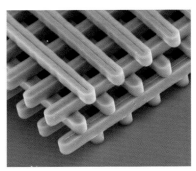

Figure 115 Photonic lattice made from silicon rods with a diameter of 1.2 micrometres
Source: Science Photo Library

structure can be guided around with minimal loss of information. Photonic lattices could be used in optical computers and communications systems.

Energy

The same properties of nanomaterials useful to sunscreens can also be exploited in photovoltaic devices. Nanocrystals absorb sunlight more effectively than conventional semiconductor material, therefore higher efficiencies can be achieved for a given surface area.

Nanocatalysts are being used to improve the efficiency of many chemical processes. In 2002 China's largest coal company, Shenhua Group, licensed technology from the US company Hydrocarbon Technologies that uses a nanoscale catalyst to liquefy coal and turn it into diesel fuel and gasoline, reducing dependence on imported oil. There are also environmental benefits as the process removes sulphur, nitrogen, ash and other impurities from the liquid fuel. The plant was due to start operating in 2005.

The economies of the industrialised world currently depend on microtechnology and in particular the microprocessor. Economic growth partly relies on performance improvements in the microprocessor. Moore's law has worked for 40 years thanks to increasingly smaller transistors on silicon chips. But there's a physical limit beyond which silicon microprocessors cease to perform. That's where nanotechnology holds promise. Research is ongoing into transistors based on organic carbon-based molecules that will take computing power to a new level.

5.2.2 Forecasting the future for nanotechnology

There are differing views about when the more advanced applications of nanotechnology, such as molecular-scale manufacturing, will finally be achieved. Thirty years ago technology optimists predicted molecular nanotechnology would have been perfected by now. But at present (2005) there are no nanobots, no molecular-scale machines and no assemblers – these are still in the basic research stages and may not be seen for decades (Figure 116). This is a technology still in its infancy but as you can see at the materials level it's already having an impact.

> What we are seeing is the beginning of a revolution, caused by our ability to work on the same scale as nature. Nanotechnology will affect every aspect of our lives, from the medicines we use, to the power of our computers, the energy supplies we require, the food we eat, the cars we drive, the buildings we live in, and the clothes we wear. And it will happen sooner than most people think. By 2010 you won't be able to count the number of businesses affected by nanotechnology.
>
> (Harper, 2003)

Like steam engines, electricity and ICT before it, nanotechnology could become a general-purpose technology (GPT) capable of having a major disruptive effect. When I explained about disruptive innovations in Section 3, I said they often started as fairly crude technologies with limited uses but with improvement ended up providing a better technological solution and replacing existing technology and

Figure 116 Imaginary nanobot manufacturing unit Source: Science Photo Library

Visualisation of a nanobot assembler designed to build self-replicating systems that could make huge manufacturing projects economically viable. Examples might include building space colonies or the terraforming of Mars.

challenging leading companies. Nanotechnology has the potential to do this on a worldwide scale.

You've seen how useful structural nanotechnology has become. You can imagine how useful molecular nanotechnology could be when it is finally achieved – making every process more economical in its use of resources, every product more efficient in doing its job. But as with any new technology there are concerns about the possible adverse impacts. At the most extreme there are nightmare visions of endlessly self-replicating nanoscale machines taking over the world, possibly at the expense of human life itself.

It's difficult to know at this early stage of its development whether such concerns about nanotechnology are realistic or fanciful. This highlights the difficulties of forecasting the future development of technology. It also points to the fact that there are optimistic and pessimistic judgements about the benefits, costs and impact of any new technology.

> From the sectors of consumer goods, vehicles, medical, computers and energy, what use of nanotechnology do you think will bring you benefits?

5.3 Technology optimism and pessimism

For technology optimists continued innovation offers easier, cheaper and more reliable ways of living and working. For technology pessimists it means an end to traditional practices, more stress and disruption. I'll consider a few examples from the area of ICT.

When the personal computer first started to spread, techno-optimists predicted it would be a liberating force that would free people from routine tasks, allow them to exercise their creativity and at the same time increase productivity. However techno-pessimists viewed the same innovation in a different light. They believed the PC would increase isolation, reduce initiative, replace individual skills and increase unemployment.

Likewise with the internet. By giving many people access to massive amounts of information the internet was seen by optimists as a force for democracy, with its unrestricted access to communication leading to a more open society. But pessimists predicted the internet would encourage people to stay at home all day accessing pornography and, more recently, downloading copyrighted music at the expense of music companies and recording artists.

While neither vision has come true completely, aspects of each vision have been realised. The PC and internet have aided individual creativity by exposing individuals to a wider range of new ideas and information, and by giving them some new techniques for solving problems and managing tasks, such as CAD software, financial packages and so on. However the PC and the internet have also introduced routine tasks of their own – filing may be electronic rather than paper-based but it still needs to be done.

And any increase in productivity is counteracted by the time spent on learning new programs, sorting out software or hardware problems and dealing with viruses and junk email. In addition the proliferation of information takes more time to manage and process and gives some people a sense of being overloaded with too much information. While it's also true that the spread of the computer has replaced some types of job a whole range of new ICT-related jobs has been created.

It's sometimes difficult to judge where the truth lies between the most optimistic and pessimistic views about the impact of technology. Technology optimists and pessimists tend to have a one-sided view of how technology is developed and used. In reality there's a complex interaction between new technology and the society using it; the technology is adapted and changed as people find different ways to use it. In the early days of most new technologies few people can imagine the long-term implications. For example, shortly after its invention, who would have imagined that we would end up using lasers for such a wide range of applications? Certainly not its inventors. So it's common to underestimate the long-term impact of many innovations. At the same time it's common to overestimate the short-term impact. When the telephone was first invented concern was expressed that unchaperoned communication would lead to the breakdown of social order and morality. Of course from some perspectives it has had that effect to some extent – what would Victorians think of phone sex? But usually society is sufficiently robust to cope with the changes that new technologies bring by adapting and moving on.

Next I'll briefly consider the environmental impact of new technologies and how society might cope, adapt and move on.

Are you a technological optimist or pessimist?

5.4 Environmental impact and sustainability

So far I've treated innovation and the development of new technology as largely an unalloyed good thing, a fundamental part of social and economic progress. The idea that economic growth, underpinned by the continued development of technology, could continue indefinitely into the future, has been increasingly challenged as the environmental impacts become more visible. Pollution, one example of environmental impact, has been problematic ever since the industrial revolution, and indeed before that.

The increasing scale of industrial and technological activity in modern times has led to an increasing range of environmental problems as well as to the prospect of shortages in key material and energy resources. While optimists argue that the environmental impacts resulting from particular technologies can be dealt with by remedial or clean-up technologies, pessimists think there is a need to reconsider the way technology is used to avoid or at least limit environmental damage. They say there is risk to the viability of the ecosystem on which social and economic systems depend.

This might seem an alarmist proposition were it not for the fact that environmental problems are no longer just a matter of local impacts from toxic emissions or wastes, important though they may be. Increasingly it has become clear that technological activities are leading to impacts on the *global* scale. The most obvious example is climate change, due primarily to so-called greenhouse gas emissions, especially carbon dioxide from the combustion of fossil fuels such as coal and oil. If unchecked, this could lead to major social and economic problems that could seriously undermine future development. This is not something a long way off. In 2003 the United Nations World Health Organisation estimated that globally at least 150 000 people were already dying each year as a result of climate change effects – drought, famine, heat stroke, increased spread of diseases like malaria. And this death rate was expected to worsen by a factor of three over the next 30 years.

In which case, as there will be impact from earlier emissions whatever we do about current emissions, there will be a need for innovations that help people to cope with and adapt to climate change – the high temperatures, floods and so on.

Adaptation is of course only part of the answer. The problem has to be dealt with at source and, in the industrialised countries at least, reducing reliance on fossil fuels will lower greenhouse gas emissions. At the same time the growing population of the developing world will need to increase its production and consumption. That in turn means there needs to be a new approach to long-term social and economic development – *sustainable development*. The concept of sustainability was given prominence by the United Nations' Brundtland Commission in its report *Our Common Future* in 1987, which included a key definition:

> Sustainable development is any development that meets the needs of the present without compromising the ability of future generations to meet their own needs.

> (World Commission on Environment and Development, 1987, p. 43)

Sustainable development involves not only taking into account the environmental impacts of technology and innovation but also social and economic aspects.

The work of the Brundtland Commission formed the basis of the United Nations Conference on Environment and Development in Rio de Janeiro in June 1992, also known as UNCED or the Earth Summit. This was the largest gathering yet of representatives of governments and non-governmental organisations and attempted to agree measures for balancing development against environmental impact. One of the key agreements adopted by the majority of the countries represented was Agenda 21. This was a 300-page plan for achieving sustainable development in the twenty-first century. It covered a range of topics regarded as vital for a sustainable future, including agriculture, deforestation, protecting the atmosphere, hazardous waste and eco-tourism. Among the wealth of detailed proposals Agenda 21 also included plans for changing patterns of production and consumption to meet basic needs while reducing environmental stress, and for promoting environmentally sound technologies.

> Environmentally sound technologies protect the environment, are less polluting, use all resources in a more sustainable manner, recycle more of their wastes and products, and handle residual wastes in a more acceptable manner than the technologies for which they were substitutes.

> (UN Department of Economic and Social Affairs, 2003)

Later in 1992 the UN established the Commission on Sustainable Development to monitor and report on the implementation of the Earth Summit agreements at all levels from local to international. This reported on a regular basis and 10 years on from the Rio summit fed into the World Summit on Sustainable Development held in Johannesburg in 2002. In the meantime a wide range of other issues had been addressed by other UN organisations. The issue of greenhouse gas emissions was addressed by the UN Framework Convention on Climate Change and led to the Kyoto Protocol, which was signed by 160 countries in 1997.

There have been major battles over the ratification of this accord, and, with the gap between rich and poor countries widening and certain aspects of environmental degradation worsening, it is arguable that the plans for sustainable development have not yet succeeded. But it is undeniable that over the past 40 years the profile of environmental issues has grown, as has the awareness of the need for a more sustainable approach to how technology will meet everyone's needs.

Ecodesign, sustainable technology and sustainable consumption will be looked at later in the course. For the present it is worth mentioning that, although environmental awareness may still not be widespread, most people in industrial countries now have some form of environmental engagement. In many areas of the UK there are council schemes for recycling waste. Consumers check the energy labels before buying a washing machine or refrigerator (Figure 117). Drivers are much more conscious of the fuel consumption and emission figures for cars than in the past.

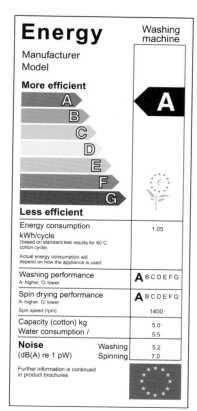

Figure 117   European Union's energy label for a domestic washing machine Source: Department for Environment, Food and Rural Affairs

A growing number are becoming ethical or green consumers with environmental issues being one of the factors shaping purchasing decisions. According to research for the Co-operative Bank Ethical Purchasing Index (Co-operative Bank, 2003), in the period from 1999 to 2002 52 per cent of consumers boycotted at least one product because they disapproved of the practices of the company concerned. It was estimated that £2.6 billion had been lost by firms in 2002 due to consumers switching brands on ethical grounds and the trend towards ethical, green and sustainable products is increasing.

Given that there can be an increasing economic benefit to companies who take environmental factors into account in the invention, design and production of new products, then more companies will have an incentive to follow a policy of sustainability. That certainly seems to be happening. In parallel governments are introducing more stringent regulations concerning the need for environmental assessment of new products.

In the last year, what environmental consideration has made you choose to purchase one product or service rather than another?

I've switched to fuel containing a proportion of biodiesel for my car.

SAQ 14

In what ways is the internet a disruptive innovation for the following areas:

(a) business transactions between companies

(b) buying a new car.

SAQ 15

In what ways might nanotechnology become a disruptive technology?

SAQ 16

In the light of the course material you've studied so far, how might individual inventors attempt to minimise the environmental impact of any new product they design?

Key points of Section 5

- Successive waves of technological innovation have had a significant impact on the way society has organised itself and has done business.

- The factors underlying major technical advances in ICT include:

  - changing from electromechanical systems to electronics

  - increasing miniaturisation allowing greater power for a given size

  - digitalisation permitting greater speeds and accuracy of data transfer

  - control of a process by software means it's easier to change and to customise.

- The internet is an example of the way a dominant technology can affect the way a society organises itself. The internet has also introduced new ways of doing business and is an example of a disruptive innovation.

- The internet developed from relatively specialised research use into a medium for mass communication due in part to the creation of adaptable, versatile software combined with the collaborative, enthusiastic approach of a growing technical community.

- Once computer control spread to business systems it became possible to control all aspects of the manufacturing process. In a commercial environment the emphasis is on increasing the speed and flexibility of the manufacturing process.

- More flexible and easily adaptable manufacturing processes have contributed to an increase in the diversity of new products and the rapidity of their obsolescence.

- Nanotechnology is the art and science of manipulating and rearranging individual atoms and molecules to create useful materials, devices and systems.

- Some real progress has been made in using nanotechnology to alter the properties of materials – structural nanotechnology. The resulting materials often display properties superior to any of their individual constituents.

- Like steam engines, electricity and ICT before it, nanotechnology could become a general-purpose technology capable of having a major effect.

- There are optimistic and pessimistic judgements about the benefits, costs and impact for a new technology. The tendency is to overestimate the short-term impact of many innovations while under-estimating their long-term impact.

- While some argue that environmental impacts can be dealt with by remedial technologies, others believe it is necessary to rethink the use of technology and thereby limit environmental damage.

- The idea that economic growth, underpinned by the continued development of technology, could continue indefinitely into the future, has been increasingly challenged as the environmental impacts became more visible.

The key points for Section 5 meet learning outcomes 1.11, 1.15, 1.16, 1.18, 2.3, 2.4 and 2.5.

6 Forecasting the future of innovation

At various stages throughout this block you've seen that it's easy to be wise about invention and innovation with hindsight. What is difficult is to identify which current inventions or innovations will succeed or fail. Many individuals and organisations are involved in this process of picking winners because the rewards of success are huge.

6.1 Survival of the fittest?

The mature products and processes in society today have had a Darwinian-like evolution involving refinement and improvement from crude beginnings. Most emerging new technologies also experience a period of competition with rivals, during which their survival can be in the balance. There is usually a range of factors that ultimately determine which technology goes on to become a winner. Take the example of one of the most successful technologies of all time, the gasoline-fuelled, internal-combustion engine. There seems to have been an inevitability about its success. But its emergence as a winning technology was by no means predictable during its early stages of development. For a while it was not clear whether steam, electric or gasoline-powered vehicles would become the most widely adopted innovation.

Now attempt the exercise below that involves reading the article 'Steam, electric and gasoline vehicles' by George Basalla before returning to the discussion below. You should expect to spend approximately 1 hour on the article and the related exercise.

Exercise 4   Factors for success or failure

As you read the extract by Basalla on 'Steam, electric and gasoline vehicles' write down any factors that seem to have influenced the success or failure of the innovations concerned.

Steam, electric, and gasoline vehicles
by George Basalla

While speculating about the state of transportation technology, [it has been hypothesised] that in a nonrail America vehicles powered by internal-combustion engines might have been developed earlier than they were. [It is] thought that some portion of the millions of dollars invested in railroads could have been diverted to the creation of an alternative mode of transportation. The time that elapsed between the understanding of the principles of the internal-combustion engine in the early nineteenth century and its embodiment in a working model in the 1860s might have been shortened were there no railways.

Throughout the nineteenth century attempts were made to produce a supplement, if not exactly an alternative, to the railroad, including a steam-powered road vehicle. Inventors in England, France, and the United States separately devised self-propelled steam cars and buses that were large, heavy, difficult to manoeuvre, and mechanically unreliable. These steam carriages, built to travel over the poorly maintained public roads of the day, could not compete with the railroad whose wheels rolled on smooth, hard metal rails. By the end of the century the steam vehicle experimenters had produced lightweight, powerful engines that, along with electric motors and gasoline engines, were used to power the first generation of automobiles [Figure 118].

Figure 118   Stanley Locomobile steam car, 1899 Source: Science Photo Library

It weighed only about 250 kilograms without water and petrol fuel. The engine and boiler were placed beneath the seat, and behind them in the enclosed boot were the feed-water tanks and smoke outlet. The driving power was transmitted by a light chain from the crankshaft using a differential gear.

At the turn of the century, it was by no means obvious that the modern automobile engine – the Otto, four-stroke cycle, internal-combustion engine – would win out over its competitors. In 1900, 4192 cars were manufactured in the United States. Of them, 1681 were steam, 1575 electric, and only 936 gasoline. Shortly thereafter, however, the internal-combustion engine began its climb to prominence. At the New York automobile show in 1901, 58 steam, 23 electric, and 58 gasoline models were put on display. By 1903 the number of steam and electric models exhibited had fallen to 34 and 51 respectively, whereas the gasoline cars numbered 168. At the 1905 exhibit the rout was complete; the 219 gasoline models displayed outnumbered by a ratio of 7 to 1 the combined total of steam and electric cars. Unfortunately, it is much easier to document the triumph of the internal-combustion engine than it is to explain its success. In 1905 each of the power plants had advantages and disadvantages; none had a clear-cut technological superiority.

The electric car appeared to have all of the good points of the horse and buggy with none of its drawbacks [Figure 119]. It was noiseless, odorless, and very easy to start and drive. No other motor vehicle could match its comfort and cleanliness or its simplicity of construction and ease of maintenance. Its essential elements were an electric motor, batteries, a control rheostat to regulate speed, and simple gearing. There was no transmission and, hence, no gears to shift.

The first commercial electric vehicles were produced in 1894. Within 5 years of their appearance on city streets, Henry Ford's boss at the Edison Illuminating Company in Detroit was urging Ford to stop wasting his time tinkering with

Figure 119   Charles Stewart Rolls (of Rolls-Royce fame) on a Barmsworth's Columbia Electric Carriage, about 1898 Source: Science Photo Library

Figure 120   Ford Model N motor car, 1906 Source: Science Photo Library

Designed by Henry Ford the Model N preceded and foreshadowed the famous Model T design. The Model N featured a light yet strong chassis, a simple, robust four-cylinder engine, and cost around $500 to buy.

gasoline engines [Figure 120]. Electricity, he argued, would provide energy for the car of the future. Inventors Elmer Sperry and Thomas Edison, who agreed with this prediction, worked on their own versions of the electric automobile. If, as many believed, the twentieth century was destined to be the electrical age, then there was no place in it for the noisy, exhaust-spewing, internal-combustion engine.

The electric car was not without serious faults. It was slow, unable to climb steep hills, and expensive to own and operate. Above all else, it had a limited cruising range. Its heavy lead and acid storage batteries had to be recharged every thirty miles or so. The electric car was not a vehicle in which to tour the countryside or drive to a distant city. The installation of battery-charging stations in Boston, Philadelphia, and New York was designed to facilitate urban travel but did not solve the problem of long-distance driving. That solution called for lighter and more powerful batteries, a goal that continues to elude electric car promoters to this day.

Because the electric vehicle's restricted operating range met the requirements of urban delivery service, electric trucks were built for the movement of goods within the city. Department stores, bakeries, and laundries purchased them as did the American Railway Express Company. Initially, electric trucks proved economical but by the mid-1920s they were displaced by delivery vehicles powered by gasoline engines, which were less expensive to purchase.

Steam automobiles enjoyed intense popularity at the beginning of the century. To understand this phenomenon, we must set them apart from the cumbersome steam carriages of the previous century. The power plant in an early twentieth-century Stanley or White steamer was a trim twenty to thirty horsepower unit, about the size of a gasoline engine, made of precision-machined steel parts, and fuelled with a petroleum product. The overall appearance of a steamer was similar to that of a gasoline motor car of the period.

The steam car was not as quiet as the electric but its purchase price and upkeep were considerably less and a powerful engine enabled it to handle all road conditions without strain. The first self-propelled vehicle to reach the summit of Mount Washington, New Hampshire, was a Stanley Steamer (1899) [Figure 118], as was the first car to travel over two miles a minute (1906). The steamers of the 1900s could outstrip the electric car but did face competition from the best of the gasoline engine automobiles.

A look at the engines of the steamer and the gasoline-powered cars points out significant differences. The steam engine's ability to deliver maximum power as it revolved at a slow and steady rate was an important factor in its success. Whereas the reciprocating internal-combustion engine in gasoline-powered cars ran at 900 revolutions per minute (rpm) when idling and 2700 rpm at maximum efficiency, the engine on the steamer at a speed of sixty miles per hour revolved at a slow 900 rpm. On internal-combustion engines an elaborate set of gearing (transmission) was necessary to transmit and transform this rotative power so that it could move the wheels at an acceptable speed, but the steamer had no need for a transmission, clutch, and gearshift. The timing, cooling, valving, and carburation of the internal-combustion engine all demanded special attention in its design and added to the number of moving parts; the steam engine had far fewer moving parts than did the gasoline engine, which meant less engine wear and easier maintenance. Finally, the use of proper fuel was critical for the gasoline engine, but low-grade petroleum distillates could be burned to heat the water of the steamer.

The steamer did have a number of important drawbacks. The limited cruising range that plagued the electric also proved troublesome for the steamer. Because steam was exhausted to the atmosphere and not condensed for reuse, the steamer needed a water refill every thirty miles. Another problem was the time it took to generate steam for the car's first run of the day, although the standard half-hour wait was eventually reduced to a few minutes with the introduction of pilot lights and flash boilers. Steam-engine builders, well aware of these shortcomings, were seeking ways to overcome them.

Steam-automobile manufacturing lasted through the 1920s and ever since then there have been periodic rumours of its revival. The most recent call for the rebirth of steam power was heard in the 1970s, a time of concern over automobile emission pollution and a petroleum shortage. How reasonable are these calls for a steam car revival? Could the steam engine have powered America's great automobile revolution of the twentieth century? Why did the steam engine fail to meet the challenge of the internal-combustion engine?

These questions become more, not less, difficult to answer when the internal-combustion engine of the 1900s is evaluated. Early gasoline motor cars were rather clumsy and complex machines. To start their engines, a hand crank and muscle power were necessary; their successful operation depended on a series of recently fashioned mechanical systems for ignition, cooling, lubrication, and transmission of power, and they were noisy and emitted unpleasant exhaust gases. On the positive side the gasoline motor car did have an extended cruising range of seventy miles, offered reliable if not trouble-free transportation, and could climb most hills and travel at a good speed on the road. Furthermore, technicians were perfecting the gasoline engine by improving its ratio of horsepower to weight. Everything considered, steam and gasoline automobiles were not that radically different in the transportation they provided.

The selection of the gasoline engine was not the result of a rational appraisal of the merits of the competing power plants. There were no automotive experts at the turn of the century, only inventors and entrepreneurs following their hunches and enthusiasms and trying to convince potential car owners to buy their product. Given this situation, once the gasoline engine gained ascendancy, steamers and electrics were either forgotten or viewed as missteps along the road to automotive progress. Thereafter, money, talent, and ideas were invested in improving the internal-combustion engine. Few were willing to champion the steam engine and fewer still to finance its improvement.

Steam and gasoline automobiles were the real contenders; the electrics had the reputation of being a car for the well-to-do and had a seemingly intractable battery problem. The steam engine suffered because of its identification with the technology of the previous century. Steam power called to mind huge locomotives or stationary engines belching black smoke, burning tons of coal, and periodically bursting their boilers. Steam scarcely seemed suitable as a motive power for a new century. In terms of modernity, electricity would have been the ideal choice, but, if it could not be had, then the internal-combustion engine seemed preferable to an updated version of the steam engine.

The one hundred or more makers of steamers did little to overcome the steam engine's negative images and thereby popularise their vehicle. The Stanley brothers, the most successful of the steam car builders, lacked the ambition and managerial skills needed to produce cars in quantity and distribute them across the nation. Nor were they quick to incorporate existing technical improvements that would have made their vehicles more attractive to customers.

In 1914 Henry Ford visited the Stanley factory, which was then turning out 650\ cars annually; Ford was manufacturing that many of his Model Ts in a single day. While skilled craftsmen slowly built and hand-finished a few Stanley steamers, unskilled workmen on Ford's innovative assembly lines were mass-producing thousands of gasoline automobiles. The Stanley Company weathered the restrictions placed by the government on the American auto industry during World War 1, but it emerged in a weakened condition. Shortly after the war, the company closed its doors; it had failed to meet the competition of the inexpensive Detroit motor car.

Some historians have cited geographical factors as the cause of the rise of the gasoline automobile. Steam and electric cars were primarily built and sold in the eastern United States. The gasoline car, on the other hand, was particularly well-suited to the rural areas of the Midwest. The midwestern predilection for gasoline cars coincided with the industrial and natural resources of the region. Its ample supply of hard woods had earlier made the Midwest a center of carriage and wagon production, and its farm power supply needs had attracted makers of stationary gasoline engines. Therefore, the Midwest could easily supply the main elements – body and engine – of the new gasoline automobile when it became a popular form of transportation.

Is there nothing more to be said about the contest between the steam and gasoline engine except that some shrewd midwestern businessmen chose the latter and used their entrepreneurial skills to make it the basis for the nation's personal transportation system? Up to this point we have not mentioned the relative efficiencies of the two engines because it was not isolated as a separate issue at the time. However, the study of theoretical and actual heat engines indicates that an Otto-cycle engine is superior in thermal efficiency to a steam engine. Consequently, everything else being equal, a gasoline engine yields more miles per gallon of fuel than a steam engine. Here, at last, is solid evidence that the promoters of the gasoline engine were on the right track. Consciously, or intuitively, they had backed the most efficient engine.

Apart from the fact that the thermal efficiency of the rival power plants was lost in the plethora of technical and cultural factors that favoured the gasoline engine, there is yet another problem. The same engineering sources that report the superior thermal efficiency of the Otto-cycle engine also disclose that the diesel engine is far more efficient than the gasoline engine. Under actual driving conditions, the average thermal efficiency of the Otto cycle is about 10 per cent and a diesel 18 per cent. Therefore, if the early Detroit entrepreneurs forsook the inefficient steam engine, why did not later, and better-informed, automotive engineers lead the country to more efficient diesel power? The answer, of course, is that the selection of automobile engines, whether in the early or late twentieth century, is made on other than purely technical and economic grounds.

A counterfactual world in which the steam engine powered automobiles and trucks is every bit as reasonable as one in which canal boats moved heavy goods cross-country or xylography served as the basis for a printing revolution. The contest between the steam and gasoline engines was a much closer one than we have been led to believe, so close that under different conditions the steam engine might have won. In America, where petroleum was cheap and plentiful, transportation could have been powered by external combustion rather than internal-combustion engines.

It is not an accident that two of the three examples of alternative technologies surveyed here are taken from modern industrial societies. Nathan Rosenberg has noted that such societies are not utterly dependent on a single innovation because, if necessary, they are capable of generating substitutes for it. If Rosenberg is correct, and there is good reason to think he is, then the examples discussed here are not unique. Alternatives can be found not only for railroads and gasoline engines but for almost any major modern invention. The production of novelty is so great that clusters of related innovations, waiting to be selected, exist to fulfil virtually any of our wants, needs, or whims. The history of technology would be written far differently if, instead of concentrating on the 'winning' innovations perpetuated by selection and replication, we were to make a diligent search for viable alternatives to those innovations.

(Source: Basalla, 1988, pp. 198–204)

Discussion

I have identified the following factors contributing to success or failure in innovation, as discussed by Basalla.

1   Attention and investment is often focused on existing successful technologies, such as railroads, delaying the development of alternatives.

2   Parallel development is required in related aspects of the same innovation *system* – such as improving the quality of public roads. (Recall the example of Edison and the lighting system in Section 1.)

3   Advantages such as comfort, cleanliness, simple construction and easy maintenance, even though they are aspects of good design, are insufficient on their own to guarantee success for an innovation if it is less successful at *meeting key needs* for the majority of potential buyers (electric cars were expensive to buy, own and operate, with a limited cruising range). In innovation, low purchase price often outweighs technological advantages for most purchasers. This relates to Rogers' factor of 'relative advantage' in understanding how rapidly innovations diffuse.

4   Image is important in the acceptance of innovations – an old-fashioned image of steam power can reduce the attractiveness to buyers. Basalla might also have mentioned the importance of good design in helping an innovation to be accepted.

5   Enthusiastic product champions are important in giving momentum to the conversion of an invention into an innovation. With fewer such champions the steam engine was less successful in competing with the gasoline engine.

6   An efficient manufacturing process is required to enable a reliable product to be produced in sufficient numbers to ensure mass availability and low purchase price, at least for mass-market products. Therefore Ford's new mass-production assembly lines were able to flood the market with low-cost, gasoline-powered cars, while steam-powered vehicles continued to be made in small numbers by a relatively expensive craft process.

7   Managerial and organisational skills are needed to produce an innovation in quantity and distribute it widely enough to improve the chances of commercial success.

8   Geographical factors can be important in the early stages of the development of an innovation. The industrial and natural resources of a particular region can make it well suited as a location for the manufacture and continued improvement of an innovation. Basalla cites this as a reason for the mass-production of the gasoline-powered car in the midwestern region of the USA with its access to appropriate materials and fuel, and its large distances that could be covered better by the gasoline car than the electric or steam vehicles. However these factors were less significant in the development of the gasoline-powered car in other parts of the world, such as Europe.

So Basalla argues that at the early stages of development of motor vehicles, although electric power suffered from lack of suitable batteries, steam engines might have become dominant if the balance of factors – technical, economic, social, cultural – had been different. There is sometimes a thin dividing line between success and failure.

Is it possible to identify a checklist of success factors that will enable us to predict whether an invention will go on to become a successful innovation?

6.2   Success factors for innovation

In 1890, when asked to give a list of requirements for success in innovation, Thomas Edison said, 'A good imagination coupled with a lot of horse sense, great application, and absolute determination never to be discouraged'. More than a 100 years later these requirements are still needed but as you've seen so far in this block there is more to it than that. What follows is not a definitive list but it does provide some criteria by which to judge likely success. You should be able to add factors to the list based on your own experience, and maybe you can add to the list as you read through the rest of the course and do your project work.

6.2.1   The inventor

- Important innovations usually emerge from the putting together of previous ideas and technology in a new way. The inventor must have the creative ability to make such unusual connections and the imagination to recognise their potential.

- Single-minded determination is important but sometimes compromise is necessary. There is the danger of an inventor becoming fixated on the technical detail and failing to appreciate the sometimes conflicting requirements that an innovation must fulfil.

- The inventor often needs to be willing to adapt the invention to meet changing manufacturing and market requirements.

- The inventor needs to consider taking out some form of protection for an invention – patent, registered design and so on. They should be prepared to spend money fighting infringement or alternatively licence the invention to a commercial company.

- A successful innovator must have some entrepreneurial abilities to sell the idea to those with the finance necessary to develop it further. Some inventors are too bound up with their ideas to take account of commercial and manufacturing requirements.

6.2.2 The invention

- It must offer obvious and significant advantages over existing products or processes, such as cheaper to make and buy, does the job better, easier to use, provides something not previously possible.

- It should be based on technically and scientifically sound principles.

- Its performance should be acceptable to the user because it does the job it's designed for and it should be reliable and safe.

- The design must be capable of being produced economically.

- Suitable materials and techniques for making it must be available.

- If the invention interacts directly with human users, it should be of acceptable appearance and be easy to maintain and use.

- It is more likely to be commercially successful if it is designed to be adaptable to different uses (robust) rather than too highly optimised and inflexible (lean).

- Launching an innovation to compete with an already well-established product or processes is risky, but the rewards of success could be great.

6.2.3 Organisational factors

- The invention must be transformed into an innovation by following a well-managed product development process.

- There must be support for the invention from an influential product champion who is able to overcome resistance by persuasion. The resistance may be from within the organisation or from outside.

- An appropriate level of finance must be available to develop the invention into a practical, marketable product.

- Process innovation is important to optimise the efficiency and cost of manufacture, and therefore to reduce the price of the product; economies of scale can also contribute to cost and price reduction.

- There are forms of organisation that can encourage invention and innovation by providing opportunities for creative teamwork.

- It is often in the interests of manufacturers to agree to common standards for manufacture, to avoid the costs and risks of unnecessary competition.

6.2.4 Diffusion factors (social, economic, political, cultural)

- The innovation must meet an existing or latent demand.

- An innovation may only become acceptable to the mass market when its early deficiencies are removed through further invention, redesign and innovation.

- The innovation should have an acceptable cost to the manufacturer, and an acceptable price and value to the customer.

- The context for innovation should be favourable. For example a company constantly trying to cut costs will be more receptive to a process innovation that reduces the cost of existing manufacture, rather than a product innovation that requires setting up a new production system.

- The innovation should be appropriate to social, economic and cultural conditions. For example following its early use for business the rapid diffusion of the mobile phone into the mass market is explained in part by cultural factors. It was a suitable product both to fulfil the need for mobile, flexible and instant communication, and to fascinate those wanting a technological gadget.

- Sometimes government legislation can provide the incentive for innovation. For example increasingly stringent legislation in the USA, Europe and Japan concerning vehicle emission levels has encouraged vehicle manufacturers to undertake R&D into innovations in propulsion technology – fuel cells, regenerative braking systems, hybrid motors – and into emission-control technology such as catalytic converters.

In many of the examples in this block it has been possible to identify certain factors that could be said to have influenced the chances of particular inventions becoming successful innovations. A brilliant idea, excellently realised in a well-designed product, developed and produced with the backing of willing financiers, helping to meet a pressing need in a receptive market, sounds too good to be true. The other side of the coin might be a less than inventive idea, inadequately realised in a poorly designed product that no one is willing to finance, and for which there appears to be no demand anyway. But of course, as you've seen, innovation is rarely as clear-cut as this.

Think back to the telephone timeline in Figure 10. Do you think if you'd been around in the early days of the telephone you could have predicted its future development?

If it is difficult to predict the likely success or failure of individual inventions and innovations, it is just as difficult to predict the future direction of innovation in general.

6.3 Forecasting technological development

Forecasting and understanding future trends in both technology and society is a crucial part of successful innovation. Forecasts can attempt to identify which technologies are possible and provide a goal for developing innovations based on those technologies. Or forecasts can attempt to predict futures into which innovations might be introduced. Forecasting is an activity that is carried out at many levels by international organisations and individuals.

- At an international level, summits and world organisations draw on a wide range of knowledge and information to try to predict trends. This information is used to shape global or regional policies and actions and to influence the direction technology will take. The Kyoto Protocol you read about in Section 5 is an example of the result of extensive predictive activity by the Intergovernmental Panel on Climate Change, which looked at likely climate trends and possible technological and policy remedies.

- At a national level governments attempt to predict trends that will shape national legislation and inform government initiatives and funding programmes. For example the trials of zero-emission, fuel-cell buses you read about in Section 2 illustrates an attempt to identify emerging technologies, assess their impact and encourage their future development in line with government strategy.

- At an intercorporate level increasingly companies are collaborating to identify trends that may lead to the creation of complex products.

- At a corporate level individual companies study trends in order to generate ideas and plan for products up to 20 years ahead.

- At an individual level some inventors and designers watch technological trends and consider their implications for developing new products or services that might become winners.

The futures that emerge from such predictive activities may appear to have a technological imperative. However in the example of the car, at each stage choices are made, by the people and organisations concerned about which technologies to take forward and which to leave behind.

In a poll to celebrate 150 years of the Patent Office, listeners to BBC Radio 4's *Today* programme voted for the best and worst inventions. The results of the poll were as follows.

Best inventions

1 bicycle – Pierre Lallement, 1866
2 radio – William Preece and Guglielmo Marconi, 1897
3 computer – Alan Turing, 1945
4 penicillin[1] – Alexander Fleming, 1928; Florey & Heatley, 1940
5 internal-combustion engine – Nicolaus August Otto, 1876
6 World Wide Web – Tim Berners-Lee, 1989
7 light bulb – Joseph Swan (UK) and Edison (USA) both in 1879
8 cat's eyes – Percy Shaw, 1935
9 telephone – Innocenzo Manzetti, 1865; Alexander G. Bell, 1876
10 television – John Logie Baird, 1923

Worst inventions

1 atomic bomb
2 land-mine
3 internal-combustion engine
4 plastic bag
5 speed camera
6 mobile phone
7 car alarm
8 television
9 tetrapak drink carton
10 Sinclair C5 vehicle

[1]Discoveries like penicillin are not patentable but methods to render them into pill form are.

While this poll is far from representative of the population as a whole it's still interesting to see it as a snapshot of the achievement of more than 100 years of invention. Because two inventions appear on both best and worst lists it also emphasises the complexity of our relationship with technology. But what would such a list look like in another 100 years? Will any of these inventions still appear or will they have been replaced by an entirely new set? It's impossible to be sure. What is your forecast?

Given the rapidity of change discussed in Section 5 it's even difficult to predict technological development over the short term. Do you recall Moore's Law? According to this prediction the number of circuits etched on a given piece of silicon could double roughly every 18 months. At this rate personal computers could become a hundred times more powerful every decade. I said in Section 5 that so far this is one of the few predictions in the area of computing that is turning out to be accurate. But even as an expert in his field, Gordon Moore himself highlighted the difficulties of predicting the future in an interview:

> I calibrate my ability to predict the future by saying that in 1980 if you'd asked me about the most important applications of the microprocessor, I probably would have missed the PC. In 1990 I would have missed the internet. So here we are just past 2000, I'm probably missing something very important.
>
> (Buderi, 2001)

Predictions of the future are inevitably rooted in the present; they tend to involve extrapolations of the way existing technologies are used (Figure 121). Predictions made in 1893 in association with the Chicago World Fair included a vision of air travel in balloons strung from wires between cities. The writer was drawing on his knowledge of existing technology, unaware of developments that would lead in 10 years time to the first aeroplane flight of the Wright brothers. Thirty years later the aeroplane itself was becoming the subject of ambitious predictions with forecasts that before the end of the twentieth century every family would own one. In the 1950s a similar prediction was made for the helicopter. And in the 1960s the US writer Marshall McLuhan predicted that by the year 2000 the wheel and the road would be obsolete, having been superseded by widespread use of the hovercraft.

McLuhan may not have been right but, in the context of our discussion earlier about how electric vehicles lost out to the petrol-driven car, it is interesting that a 100 years on electric vehicles are making a comeback. The new technology is different however. Traditional battery technology is just beginning to be replaced by fuel cells running on hydrogen and ultimately the hydrogen may be produced using electricity generated using renewable energy sources. The factors supporting the changeover are also different from those that led to the eventual dominance of petrol engines.

The idea of shifting to a so-called hydrogen economy has been touted for many years and fuel cells were invented over 100 years ago. But it has taken some major environmental and political shocks to make this option seem realistic. Rather than direct economic and operational factors (cheapness and convenience) environmental factors have come to the fore. Reserves of oil will not last forever and the use of petrol and diesel in vehicles creates local and global environmental problems.

Figure 121 The computer, as imagined in 1927, did not anticipate the miniaturisation made possible by the integrated circuit and the microprocessor Source: Mary Evans Picture Library

Moreover getting access to the reserves that are left is facing developed countries with increasing political problems.

So not only has the technology changed but so have the social, economic, political and cultural constraints – the context in which innovation takes place.

So it can be difficult to predict exactly when circumstances will change to make an existing technology suddenly viable. And the detail of technological development itself is difficult to predict because, by definition, invention contains a surprise element, something new that didn't exist previously. You've already seen earlier how new technologies can emerge and have an unexpected impact on society.

For example who before the 1940s could have predicted the impact of the invention of computers? Even those few mathematicians and scientists involved in the pioneering work that would lead to the computer would almost certainly be amazed at the extent to which it pervades so many aspects of modern life. In fact even as late as the end of the 1960s predictions about the future were being made with no reference to computers.

On the other hand it is sometimes possible to make an inspired prediction that is not based on any clues from existing technology. Recall the Punch cartoon from 1879 (Figure 68) that seemed to predict the videophone almost 100 years ahead of the technology.

Given the nature of inventions and the unanticipated developments of known technology, predicting what will be the innovative technologies of the future is clearly problematic. Yet a key theme that emerges from an historical study of the development of technology is *continuity*.

Despite appearances novel products and processes rarely turn up 'out of the blue' but rather build upon existing artefacts or ways of doing things – there is continuity. Some improvements on what exists may be significant enough to be labelled radical – such as the steam engine and lasers – and up to a certain moment in time are unpredictable. A close examination of even radical innovations, however, reveals stages in their development that built on preceding products, processes or theories, on the prior work of multitudes of individual inventors, craft workers, engineers, designers, entrepreneurs and, in the modern world, marketing experts, managers and financiers.

So, many of the innovative technologies that are expected to be important in the future, for example nanotechnology, exist now in some form. Many will involve incremental improvements to existing technology. Others might be more radical, and involve unexpected applications of a scientific discovery, or imaginative combinations of existing unrelated technologies. These more radical innovations and their disruptive impact on society are much more difficult to predict. This has not stopped people from trying. For example the UK has followed the lead of Japan and has established a Technology Foresight programme aimed at trying to identify trends that should be followed up. The first round of the exercise involved 15 panels of experts looking 20 years ahead to see what technologies might be relevant. It was completed, following a major consultation exercise, in 1995 and identified a range of areas in which, it was suggested, public and private sector resources might usefully be invested – solar photovoltaic energy technology was one example. The next UK Technology Foresight exercise looked further ahead, by 40 years, and culminated in a series of reports in 2000. One suggestion was that there should be more emphasis on fuel cells and other micro-power devices. Subsequently more reports have emerged, looking at the possible trends sector by sector.

Increasingly in such studies use has been made of socio-economic scenarios, to set the scene for a discussion of which technologies might be relevant. This is in recognition of the fact that technology is not the only issue and society is far from a static thing. Needs, wants, expectations and habits change, in part due to the impacts of new technologies and this changing context may influence the success or otherwise of other new technologies. Environmental constraints and climate change concerns have also increasingly been included in these attempts to map out options for the future and to develop ideas for what a sustainable future might look like.

The DVD contains a presentation called 'SusHouse: Strategies towards the Sustainable Household'. This is one example of the use of scenarios to anticipate how a more environmentally sustainable future might look for household functions such as shopping, cooking and eating, cleaning clothes or providing shelter, and how the development of particular products or services might bring about a given scenario. This material might be useful to you in developing ideas for your project topic.

Identifying trends and desired goals like this are in no way predictions – at best they just identify options. If the future direction of technology can't be predicted, can society at least make sure it goes in a direction where the benefits of innovation outweigh the costs and where continued development is socially, economically and environmentally sustainable? These questions are addressed at various points throughout the course. However past experience shows that when a new product or process achieves a certain momentum the innovation process will take off, and once it does, it can be difficult to control and impossible to turn back. I think there is that kind of momentum now with more innovations than at any time in history – which is both an exciting and a challenging prospect.

Key points of Section 6

- Most emerging new technologies experience a period of competition with rivals, during which their survival can be in the balance.

- Factors that determine which technology goes on to become a winner relate to the characteristics of the invention and the inventor, the way development and manufacture are organised, and the social, economic, environmental, political and cultural factors that affect diffusion.

- Even radical innovations build on preceding products, processes or theories, on the prior work of multitudes of individual inventors, craft workers, engineers, designers, entrepreneurs; and, in the modern world, marketing experts, managers and financiers.

- Forecasting and understanding future trends in both technology and society is a crucial part of successful innovation.

- Continued development is only sustainable if the benefits of innovation outweigh the costs.

The key points for Section 6 meet learning outcomes 1.17, 1.18, 2.2 and 2.5.

Answers to self-assessment questions

SAQ 1

Given the definitions above, would you classify the following as an invention or an innovation?

(a) BIC ballpoint pen – innovation.

It is an innovation that not only reached the market – initially the military then the civilian market – but also went on to achieve great commercial success and become widely diffused throughout society.

(b) Flettner's rotor ship – between invention and innovation.

This example is on the boundary between an invention and an innovation. It reached the working prototype stage but arguably not quite the point of first commercial use, with only one ship being commissioned by a third party.

(c) Edison's tinfoil phonograph – invention.

It was the wax cylinder version that went on to be sold as an innovation.

(d) Edison's bamboo-filament light bulb – innovation.

It was the dominant design used in the early commercialisation of the light bulb, compared with the carbonised cotton used in the initial invention.

SAQ 2

Would you classify the following as examples of radical innovation or incremental innovation?

(a) Edison's phonograph – radical.

Radical in that nothing like it had existed before. It caused quite a stir at the time and since has had a widespread impact on the lives of generations of people. The initial invention made use of existing technology but in a radical way. The next 100 years saw steady incremental improvements in the technology.

(b) Compact fluorescent lamps – incremental.

Incremental in that they didn't involve a major new step in the development of the technology but rather involved technical improvements to an existing product. However these were important improvements as they have gained an increasing share of the domestic lighting market.

(c) Edison's electric light – radical.

Radical in terms of its eventual impact if less so in terms of its technology. Its ultimate success was dependent on incremental developments in many related areas of technology, for example vacuum pumps.

(d) Bell's telephone – radical in some ways.

It was certainly radical in terms of its eventual impact on individuals and the organisation of society. But like Edison and the electric light, when you look closely at the development of the technology, you can see how it built incrementally on existing technologies and ideas.

These answers illustrate the blurring of the boundary between the two categories. Often the radical nature of an innovation lies in the original idea to use technology to do something previously unknown or never before achieved. The subsequent transformation of a radical invention into a practical innovation depends on incremental improvements in many aspects of the related technology. The two concepts are inter-related.

SAQ 3

What are the four criteria that must be satisfied for an inventor to be granted a patent on an invention?

For an inventor to be granted a patent, an invention:

(a) must be *new* – the idea must never have been disclosed publicly in any way, anywhere, prior to the claim being filed

(b) must *involve an inventive step* – the idea must not be obvious to someone with a good knowledge and experience of the subject

(c) must be *capable of industrial application* – the invention can take the physical form of a substance, product, or apparatus; or it must be an industrial type of process

(d) must *not be excluded* – an invention is not patentable if it is of a type listed as specifically excluded, although such lists vary in different countries.

SAQ 4

What are the four main factors that motivate individuals to invent?

Individuals are motivated to invent by one or more factors:

(a) scientific or technical curiosity

(b) constructive discontent about the way a technological product performs

(c) desire to help others

(d) desire to make money.

SAQ 5

What are the four main factors that motivate organisations to invent?

Organisations are motivated to invent by one or more factors:

(a) as part of a chosen business strategy

(b) the need to improve existing products and processes

(c) the appearance of new materials, technologies and manufacturing processes

(d) government policy, legislation and regulations.

SAQ 6

From the brief description of Carlson's invention of xerography given above, how do the five key steps of the Usher–Lawson model fit that particular example?

(a) *Identification of the problem*. Carlson was dissatisfied with existing methods of copying documents by photography and by hand.

(b) *Exploration*. Carlson consulted existing patents and other information in a search for a solution to the problem.

(c) *Incubation*. The brief account above doesn't give any detail about the precise creative process involved in this invention.

(d) *Act of insight*. Carlson's act of insight involved the 'transfer' of techniques quite different from conventional photography and not previously used for copying. This is an example that shows that insight doesn't always come in a flash.

(e) *Critical revision*. Carlson's first electrostatic copier was the outcome of almost 10 years of developing and refining the technology. This process of critical revision is still going on more than 50 years after the launch of the innovation.

SAQ 7

To what extent would you describe the following inventions as predominantly arising from technology push or from market pull?

(a) Early motor cars – push.

The invention of the motor car involved technology push with enthusiasts trying to improve the technology and persuade people of the viability of the invention. It was regarded as a toy until improved performance and falling price made it an attractive product and market pull became an important factor encouraging further innovation.

(b) Car airbags – pull.

Predominantly pull, arising out of the need for greater safety.

(c) Photocopier – pull and push.

It has been subject to both pull and push. It started with the pull from the need to improve the method of copying documents. Once the technology had been developed it had to be 'pushed' onto a market that was uncertain of its need for the innovation.

(d) High-yielding varieties of wheat and rice – pull and push.

Pull was from the human need to feed people more efficiently and the economic incentive to capture a share of a steady market. Push was from the outcome of scientific research into biotechnology and gene manipulation opening up new possibilities.

(e) Laser – push.

Predominantly push because it arose out of mathematical theory and scientific research and in the early stages of its development had no obvious application. Only later, as possible uses began to be realised, did pull begin to provide an incentive for further improvements to meet the emerging needs of new applications in medicine, industry and commerce.

These examples suggest the innovation process involves elements of both push and pull at different stages. Sometimes both are at work at the same time when there is a coupling between push and pull.

SAQ 8

A dramatic example of the importance of process innovation for a product's success is mentioned in subsection 1.1 of this block. What is it?

Subsection 1.1 contains an advertisement showing that the early ballpoint pens were on sale for approximately half the weekly wage of the time. A key contribution to this product made by Baron Bich was to develop a manufacturing process capable of reducing production costs and sales price significantly. The BIC disposable ballpoint pen now costs a few pence.

SAQ 9

Rogers gives five characteristics of an innovation that affect how well it will sell and how quickly it will diffuse. Briefly use these characteristics to explain the rapid diffusion of the mobile phone.

- *Relative advantage*. The main competitive advantage of the mobile phone is its very mobility. It freed people from having to find a public phone if they needed to make a call when travelling. This proved an attractive feature to business people and also for use in emergencies. As the network spread to near universal coverage (in the UK) the relative advantage increased. For some people cost, compared with landline telephones, is a factor preventing even more rapid diffusion.

- *Compatibility*. Mobile phones fulfilled people's need for rapid and instant communication, at first for business then increasingly for social purposes. They were also compatible with the image of the use of technical gadgets reflecting the modernity of the user. Resistance to purchase comes from those who don't find this image attractive and find the mobile phone intrusive – they'd rather keep the world at bay.

- *Complexity*. Mobile phones are relatively easy to understand and use for those who are familiar with and confident users of technological gadgets. This explains the high take up among young users. As the technology has developed some mobiles are getting more complex in terms of their functions, but with the aid of good design they are easy enough to operate. Some people won't buy a mobile because they see them as complex devices.

- *Observability*. The extent to which mobile phones can be seen being used by others has certainly been a factor in their diffusion. They are observable products, being used in public more often than most innovations. Once again this very observability has probably led to some resistance from potential buyers.

- *Trialability*. As with many new products, the extent to which mobile phones can be tried out before purchase is limited. Apart from an in-store demonstration, borrowing someone's mobile for a call might be the only opportunity to try the product before purchase. Once tied into a contract users can change to a different mobile handset, but trialability doesn't seem to have been a significant factor in the diffusion of the mobile phone.

SAQ 10

Would you classify the following as examples of sustaining innovation or disruptive innovation?

(a) Cordless domestic phones – largely sustaining.

Cordless domestic phones offered an improvement to the performance of existing handsets. The ending of BT's monopoly had already led to the appearance of more companies offering a variety of handsets. The arrival of cordless handsets on the market continued this process rather than launching a new wave of innovation.

(b) Mobile phones – disruptive.

The development of mobile telephones led to a new way of operating in the telecommunications market. Mobile telephony challenged existing companies to decide whether to ignore or embrace such new developments. Many new companies arose to exploit the market at the expense of existing telephone providers.

(c) Edison's electric light – disruptive.

As well as establishing a completely new industry based around the provision of 'electric candles' Edison's invention required the creation of systems for the delivery of electricity to homes and businesses. This in turn enabled an outlet for the invention of a wide range of products designed to make use of this delivered electricity. Entire new industries grew up around this principle, making the electric light a truly disruptive innovation.

(d) Compact fluorescent lamps – sustaining.

Compact fluorescents offered technical improvements to an existing product. They've created a new market niche rather than opening up an entirely new market.

SAQ 11

Recall what Section 3 said about overcoming obstacles to innovation. What were the main technical, financial and organisational obstacles facing Craig Johnston's improved soccer boot? How were these obstacles overcome?

Technical obstacles. There was a need for the best combination of materials properties and manufacturing method. It was met by the company developing a new rubber compound and an appropriate manufacture and assembly process.

Financial obstacles. Developing the prototype as far as he did cost Johnston £250 000. Despite being relatively affluent for an inventor he was still unable to fund the cost of taking the boot to market. The obstacle was overcome by sports firm Adidas recognising the advantage the boot offered and being confident it could recoup its development costs and make a significant profit from sales.

Organisational obstacles. The not-invented-here attitude and the innovative nature of the design of the prototype were obstacles. They were overcome by a willingness to carry out practical tests on the prototype and resistance disappeared after good test results. Compromise on features of the original made the final design closer to existing boots and more acceptable to the market.

SAQ 12

Can individuals working in teams in large organisations be creative or do organisations tend to restrict individual creativity?

In Section 4 you saw how Jewkes and his colleagues suggested that organisations can restrict the sort of individual creativity vital for invention by placing constraints on behaviour. Organisations need a degree of order and predictability to function. In contrast, at least in the early stages of invention, the mind of an individual inventor needs to roam freely without being curtailed by commercial considerations, such as the requirement to develop specific products for the market. However the example of the Post-it shows that creativity can be managed within an organisation. 3M achieved the best of both worlds by creating an environment within which individuals could behave for part of their time as individual inventors, yet combining this with the benefits of teamwork and resources.

SAQ 13

Is it inevitable that government or large commercial organisations will always be the key players in developing and financing innovation?

Yes, to the extent that mass-market innovation requires large-scale investment of resources that could be years ahead of profit from sales. However it does depend on the nature and type of technology involved. What I might call low-technology inventions such as the Workmate are more likely to permit the involvement of individual inventors than high-technology innovations like the laser. Various examples in this block have shown that individuals still have a role to play in innovation, but it is more likely to be as providers of inventive ideas, solutions to manufacturing problems, and so on rather than in providing the necessary financial support for development, production and marketing.

Most individuals or small companies cannot afford to sustain the development costs of an innovation for too long before reaping some financial benefit – unless they are cushioned by income from another source. For example James Dyson was able to fund development work on his cyclone vacuum cleaner from the proceeds of an earlier invention – the Ballbarrow. Within a government research laboratory or large commercial organisation the sort of exploratory work necessary for development can occur without immediate pressures for short-term return on investment. Nevertheless critics of existing R&D policy in government and industry suggest that there is now insufficient long-term research taking place because of commercial pressures by investors for quick profits, especially in the UK.

SAQ 14

In what ways is the internet a disruptive innovation for the following areas.

(a) *Business transactions between companies.* As most businesses now have a website and an internet connection, transferring electronic documents from one company to another with reasonable security has become routine. The cost-savings in online procurement can be considerable. The world's leading automobile manufacturers now insist that all their suppliers do web transactions, so traditionalist companies that fail to modernise by embracing the internet are likely to lose out to smaller, more flexible competitors.

(b) *Buying a new car.* The internet makes it feasible for existing car manufacturers to sell direct to the public and bypass conventional car dealerships. ICT and the increase in connectivity means consumers can now choose a model and specification and buy direct from a manufacturer's website without interacting with sales staff. These orders can be placed directly and the availability of cars made known to the customer, again through the internet without the need for a salesperson. Also new internet-based companies like JamJar Cars have emerged to challenge traditional showroom-based car dealers. This does not mean all car dealerships will disappear. Nor will the change happen overnight because people have developed the habit of buying a car in a certain way. But there's no doubt it has stirred up the existing system and in the long term the changes may be more dramatic.

SAQ 15

In what ways might nanotechnology become a disruptive technology?

Disruptive technology often starts as a series of fairly crude innovations with limited uses, but with improvement ends up providing a better technological solution, replacing existing technology and challenging leading companies. Nanotechnology has the potential to do this on a worldwide scale. Starting with relatively simple current applications in stain-repellent trousers, car bumper composition and more effective sunscreen, nanotechnology is likely to spread into every aspect of our lives. It could have a part to play in medicines we use, our computers, energy supplies we require, food we eat, cars we drive, buildings we live in, and the clothes we wear.

The companies currently providing such products will be faced with the decision to continue working with existing technologies and methods of production or trying to embrace the new disruptive technology. Some established companies will lose out to newer, smaller, more flexible and more adventurous competitors. At the same time businesses relying on the existing industrial infrastructure will lose out if the industry changes – for example glass bottle manufacturers will lose out if there is a move to nano-engineered plastic bottles.

SAQ 16

In the light of the course material you've studied so far, how might individual inventors attempt to minimise the environmental impact of any new product they design?

(a) Assess the need for a new product.

Before going too far, inventors can ask themselves whether their idea is likely to fulfil a genuine need for a new or improved product. Adding to the proliferation of incremental inventions might mean adding to the overall environmental impact of new products unnecessarily.

(b) Design the product to be more efficient.

Regularly review the design of a product as it develops, aiming where possible for simplification and integration. Can the product be redesigned with fewer parts? Can parts be designed to serve more than one function? Can a new or different principle be used? Can parts be redesigned for ease of fabrication? Can fasteners be eliminated or reduced by using tabs or snap-fits? Can a product be designed to use standard components?

(c) Choose materials with sustainability in mind.

When choosing the materials for their new product inventors could take account of the energy consumed and pollution produced in the extraction and preprocessing of raw materials as well as their final processing into a product. They could also consider the effect of chosen materials on the life of the product and the potential for recycling and environmentally sound disposal at the end of the product's life.

(d) Consider the impact of manufacturing and distribution.

Choose manufacturing and assembly processes that achieve efficiency by minimising the number of components and stages, and regularly review the chosen processes. More efficiency equates with lower impact. You saw in Section 5 how careful coordination of the manufacturing, delivery and sales processes can reduce the amount and therefore the environmental impact of transportation.

You might make use of the above ideas in your project work.

References and further reading

Basalla, G. (1988) *The Evolution of Technology*, Cambridge, Cambridge University Press.

Baylis, T. (2000) *Clock This: My Life as an Inventor*, London, Headline.

Bell, D. (1988) 'The third technological revolution and its possible socio-economic consequences' (third annual faculty lecture), Salford, University of Salford.

Bell Labs (1998) *Winning the Nobel Prize*, [online], Lucent Technologies. Available from: www.bell-labs.com/history/laser/invention/invention9.html (accessed 8 July 2005).

Bennett, R.C. and Cooper, R.G. (1979) 'Beyond the marketing concept', *Marketing*, December, pp. 76–83.

Buderi, R. (2001) 'Laying Down the Law', *Technology Review*, May 2001 [online], Technology Review Inc. Available from: www.technologyreview.com (accessed 8 July 2005).

Christensen, C.M. (2003) *The Innovator's Dilemma: The Revolutionary Book that will Change the Way You do Business*, New York, HarperCollins.

Clark, R.W. (1977) *Edison: The Man who Made the Future*, London, Macdonald and Jane's.

Clarke, A.C. (1968) *The Promise of Space*, London, Hodder and Stoughton.

The Co-operative Bank, (2003) *Ethical Purchasing Index 2003*.

DaimlerChrysler (2003) *DaimlerChrysler Delivers the First Fuel Cell Bus to the City of Madrid* [online], DaimlerChrysler AG. Available from: www.daimlerchrysler.com (accessed 23 January 2004).

Denning, P.J. (ed) (2002) *The Invisible Future: The Seamless Integration of Technology into Everyday Life*, New York, McGraw-Hill.

Department of Trade and Industry (2003) *Competing in the global economy: the innovation challenge*, Innovation report, December 2003, pp. 3–8.

Douthwaite, B. (2002) *Enabling Innovation: A Practical Guide to Understanding and Fostering Technological Change*, London, Zed Books.

Drucker, P.F. (1985) *Innovation and Entrepreneurship: Practice and Principles*, London, Heinemann.

Evans, P. and Wurster, T.S. (2000) *Blown to Bits: How the New Economics of Information Transforms Strategy*, Boston MA, Harvard Business School Press.

Evans-Pughe, C. (2003) 'The cyberserfs', *The Independent*, 19 November.

Friedel, R., Israel, P. and Finn, B.S. (1987) *Edison's Electric Light: Biography of an Invention*, New Brunswick NJ, Rutgers University Press.

Gelatt, R. (1977) *The Fabulous Phonograph 1877–1977* (2nd edn), London, Cassell.

Giscard d'Estaing, V. (ed) (1991) *The Book of Inventions and Discoveries*, London, Macdonald & Co.

Gorman, M.E. and Carlson, W.B. (1990) 'Interpreting invention as a cognitive process: the case of Alexander Graham Bell, Thomas Edison, and the telephone', in *Science, Technology and Human Values*, vol. 15, no. 2, pp. 31–164.

Haberman, M. (2002) *Diary of an Inventor* [online]. Available from: www.mandyhaberman.com (accessed 24 February 2005).

Harper, T. (2003) 'Riding the tiger: the ethics of nanotechnology', *Nanotechnology Now*, August 2003 [online], 7thWave Inc. Available from: www.nanotech-now.com/products/nanonewsnow (accessed 23 March 2005).

Heskett, J. (1980) *Industrial Design*, London, Thames & Hudson.

Howard, M. (2002) 'Key findings of the 3DayCar' [online], ALTA. Available from: www.alta.net/fs_alta/publicfiles/3daycar%20-%20mickey%20howard.ppt (accessed 2 May 2002).

Hughes, T.P. (1991) 'From Deterministic Dynamos to Seamless-web Systems' in Sladovich, H.E. and Holloman, J.H. (eds), *Engineering as a Social Enterprise*, Washington DC, National Academy Press.

Hunkin, T. (1990) *Almost Everything there is to Know*, London, Hamlyn.

Huws, U. (2003) *The Making of a Cybertariat: Virtual Work in a Real World*, London, Merlin.

Internet Magazine (2003) (no longer published).

Internet Magazine (2004) (no longer published).

Jaffe, D. (2003) *Ingenious Women: From Tincture of Saffron to Flying Machines*, Stroud, Sutton.

Jewkes, J., Sawers, D. and Stillerman, R. (1969) *The Sources of Invention* (2nd edn), London, Macmillan.

Koestler, A. (1989) *The Act of Creation*, London, Arkana.

Lawson, B. (1990) *How Designers Think*, London, Architectural Press.

Lucky, R.W. (1991) 'Pondering the Unpredictability of the Sociotechnical System' in Sladovich, H.E. and Holloman, J.H. (eds), *Engineering as a Social Enterprise*, Washington DC, National Academy Press.

Lyman, P. and Varian H.R. (2003) *How Much Information?*, Berkley CA, School of Information Management and Systems, University of California.

Margolis, J. (2001) *A Brief History of Tomorrow: The Future, Past and Present*, London, Bloomsbury.

Macaulay, D. and Ardley, N. (1988) *The Way Things Work*, Dorling Kindersley.

Martin, P. (2002) 'Patently absurd: why hasn't anybody invented a way to support British inventors?' *Sunday Times Magazine*, 14 July.

Moore, G.E. (1965) 'Cramming more components onto integrated circuits', *Electronics*, vol. 38, no. 8, 19 April, pp. 114–17.

Morita, A., Reingold, E.M. and Shimomura, M. (1986) *Made in Japan*, London, Collins.

McNeil, I. (1990) *An Encyclopaedia of the History of Technology*, London, Routledge.

NUA.com (2005) *How Many Online?*, [online], Available from: www.nua.ie/surveys/how_many_online (accessed 7 April 2005).

Open University (1995) T204 *Design: Principles and Practice*, Block 5, 'Product development and manufacture: the design and engineering of cars', Milton Keynes, The Open University.

Petroski, H. (1999) *Remaking the World: Adventures in Engineering*, New York, Vintage Books.

Petroski, H. (2002) *Invention by Design: How Inventors get from Thought to Thing*, Cambridge MA, Harvard University Press.

Pilditch, J. (1978) 'How Britain can compete', *Marketing*, December, pp. 34–8.

Rensselaer Polytechnic Institute (1998) 'Electrodeless Lamps', *Lighting Futures*, vol. 1, no. 1, [online]. Available from: http://www.lrc.rpi.edu/programs/Futures/LF-Electrodeless/index.asp (accessed 2 May 2002).

Rolt, L.T.C. (1970) *Victorian Engineering*, London, Allen Lane.

Rogers, E.M. (2003) *Diffusion of Innovations* (5th edn), London, Simon & Schuster.

Rose, M.A. (1991) *The Post-modern and the Post-industrial: A Critical Analysis*, Cambridge, Cambridge University Press.

Rosenfeld, R. and Servo, J.C. (1990) 'Facilitating innovation in large organizations', in M.A. West and J. Farr (eds), *Innovation and creativity at work: Psychological and organizational strategies*, Chichester, Wiley.

Rothwell, R. (1992) 'Development towards the fifth generation model of innovation', *Technology Analysis and Strategy Management*, vol. 4, no. 1, Carfax Publishing Company.

Open University (2004) T211 *Design and designing*, Block 3, Milton Keynes, The Open University.

Shabi, R. (2003) 'The card up their sleeve', *the Guardian Weekend*, 19 July [online]. Available from: www.guardian.co.uk/weekend (accessed 7 July 2005).

Standage, T. (1999) *The Victorian Internet: The Remarkable Story of the Telegraph and the Nineteenth Century's Online Pioneers*, London, Phoenix.

Teece, D.J. (1986) 'Profiting from technological innovation: Implications for integration, collaboration, licensing and public policy', *Research Policy*, vol. 15, pp. 285–305.

Tibballs, G. (1994) *The Guinness Book of Innovations: The 20th Century from Aerosol to Zip*, Enfield, Guinness.

Uldrich, J. and Newberry, D. (2003) *The Next Big Thing Is Really Small: How Nanotechnology Will Change The Future Of Your Business*, New York, Crown Business.

UN Department of Economic and Social Affairs (2003) *Agenda 21*, [online], New York, NY, Division for Sustainable Development. Available from: www.un.org/esa/sustdev (Accessed 19 January 2005).

Usher, A.P. (1954) *A History of Mechanical Inventions* (revised edn), Cambridge MA, Harvard University Press.

Utterback, J.M. (1994) *Mastering the Dynamics of Innovation: How Companies Can Seize Opportunities in the Face of Technological Change*, Boston, MA, Harvard Business School Press.

van Dulken, S. (2002) *Inventing the 20th Century: 100 Inventions that Shaped the World*, London, British Library.

Walter, D. (1992) *Today Then: America's Best Minds Look 100 Years into the Future on the Occasion of the 1893 World's Columbian Exposition*, Helena MT, American and World Geographic Publishing.

Winston, B. (1998) *Media Technology and Society: A History – From the Telegraph to the Internet*, London, Routledge.

World Commission on Environment and Development (1987) *Our Common Future (Brundtland report)*, Oxford, Oxford University Press.

Acknowledgements

Grateful acknowledgement is made to the following sources for permission to reproduce material within this book:

Text

Pages 161–166: Basalla, G., (1988), 'Steam, Electric, and Gasoline Vehicles', *The Evolution of Technology*, published by Cambridge University Press, reprinted with permission of the author and Cambridge University Press.

Pages 117–120: Courtesy of Mandy Haberman.

Figures

Figure 1: © Mirrorpix. Figures 2 and 77: © DIY Picture Library. Figure 3: Courtesy of Dyson (UK) Ltd. Figures 4 and 83: © John Frost Historical Newspapers. Figures 5, 8l, 22, 39, 54, 88: Richard Hearne/ Open University. Figures 6, 7a, 7b: © Science Photo Library. Figures 8a, 8b, 8c, 8d, 8e, 8f, 8g, 8j, 12, 20, 31, 40, 41, 42, 45, 72, 73, 74, 76, 80, 81, 82, 89, 118, 119, 120: © The Science Museum / Science & Society Picture Library. Figure 8h: Source unknown. Figure 8i: © Sam Hallas. Figure 8k: © P.M. Northwood / Northwood Images. Figures 9, 13, 14, 69: E. Taylor/Open University. Figure 11: Courtesy of Mike Fletcher – Telephones UK. Figures 15, 16, 19: © US Dept of the Interior, National Park Service, Edison National Historic Site. Figures 17, 18, 21, 62: © The Smithsonian Institute. Figure 23: © Courtesy of Philips Lighting BV. Figure 24: Patent Specifications 1267032 'Workbench', © Crown Copyright. Reproduced with the permission of the controller of Her Majesty's Stationery Office. Figure 25a: © Hulton Archive / Getty Images. Figure 25b: © Corbis/Hulton Deutsch Collection. Figure 26: © Alexis Rosenfield / Science Photo Library. Figure 27e: © Paul Shambroom / Science Photo Library. Figure 27c: © BSIP Laurent / Science Photo Library. Figure 27b: © Philippe Plailly / Eurelios / Science Photo Library. Figure 27a: © Antonia Reeve / Science Photo Library. Figure 27d: © Rosenfeld Images Ltd / Science Photo Library. Figure 29: Courtesy of the Hovercraft Museum Trust. Figure 30: Courtesy of Hovercraft Consultants Ltd. Figure 32: © Martin Dohrn / Science Photo Library. Figure 33: © Courtesy of Textron Systems, Marine & Land Operations. Figure 34: © Dyson (UK) Ltd. Figure 35: © Rank Xerox (UK) Ltd. Figures 36 and 37: From: S. van Dulken, 'Inventing the 20th Century', The British Library Board, London 2002. Figures 38a and 38b: © Courtesy of Reflecto Ltd. Figure 43: © Pascal Goetgheluck / Science Photo Library. Figure 44: © Torben Lenau / Nitinol Devices & Components Inc. Figure 46: © Courtesy of Omron Electronics Ltd. Figure 48: © David Parker / Science Photo Library. Figure 49: Courtesy of Ford of Britain. Figure 50: © Courtesy of EvoBus (UK) Ltd. Figure 52: © Flymo (UK) Ltd. Figure 53: Courtesy of Renault (UK) Limited. Figures 55 and 56: © Eye of Science / Science Photo Library. Figure 57: Crown copyright, reproduced with permission from the Controller HMSO. Figure 58: Courtesy of the Raytheon Company. Figures 59 and 98: US Dept of the Interior, National Parks Service, Edison National Historic Site.

Figure 61: © Sony (UK) Ltd. Figure 63: US Patent 2,040,248, May 12, 1936, Dvorak, A. et al., "Typewriter Keyboard". Figure 65: © TRL Ltd. / Science Photo Library. Figure 66: © Science Photo Library. Figure 67: Rothwell, R. (1992) 'Developments towards the fifth generation model of innovation', Technology Analysis and Strategy Management, Carfax Publishing Company. Figure 68: © Punch Cartoon Library. Figures 70 and 71: © Ronald Gelatt. From R. Gelatt, 'The Fabulous Phonograph', 2nd edn, Cassell & Co. Ltd. 1977. Figure 75: © John Frost Newspaper Service. Figure 78: © Copyright Black and Decker Inc., 2004; reproduced with permission. Figure 79: Permission to reproduce extracts from BS 1363: 1995 Part 2 is granted by BSI. British Standards can be obtained from BSI Customer Services, 389 Chiswick High Road, London W4 4AL. Tel: +44 (0)20 8996 9001. Email: cservice@bsi-global.com. Figure 84: Courtesy of Apple Computer Inc. Figure 85: © Alex Bartel / Science Photo Library. Figure 87a: © Hulton Archive. Figure 87b: Courtesy of BT Archives. Figure 87c: Courtesy of BT (UK) Ltd. Figure 87d: © NEC2001–2004. Courtesy of NEC (UK) Ltd. Figures 90a and 90b: © Courtesy of Mandy Haberman. Figure 91: Haberman, M., (1997), International Patent Application for Drinks Containers. Crown copyright, Reproduced with permission from the Controller HMSO. Figures 92 and 93: © BBC Education. Figure 94: © Kieran Doherty / Reuters. Figure 95: © Toby Melville / Reuters. Figure 96: © Volker Steger / Science Photo Library. Figure 97: From: S. van Dulken, 'Inventing the 20th Century', The British Library Board, London 2002. Figure 99: © Rex Features. Figure 100: Courtesy of Trevor Bayliss. Figure 101: © Los Alamos National Laboratory / Science Photo Library. Figure 102: © Geoff Tomkinson / Science Photo Library. Figure 103: Courtesy of Vismedia / BT. Figure 104a: Copyright © Richard Hearne / Fujifilm. Figure 104b: © Sony (UK) Ltd. Figure 105: © Hank Morgan / Science Photo Library. Figure 106: © Mehau Kulyk / Science Photo Library. Figure 107: Copyright © Richard Hearne. Figure 108: © Tom McHugh / Science Photo Library. Figure 109: © Maximilian Stock Ltd / Science Photo Library. Figure 110: © Manfred Kage / Science Photo Library. Figure 111: © Courtesy of Universal Display Corporation. Figure 112: © Volker Steger / Science Photo Library. Figure 113: © Volker Steger / Sandia National Laboratory / Science Photo Library. Figure 114: © Hewlett-Packard Laboratories / Science Photo Library. Figure115: © Sandia National Laboratories / Science Photo Library. Figure 116: © Roger Harris / Science Photo Library. Figure 117: Crown copyright material is reproduced under Class Licence Number C01W0000065 with the permission of the Controller of HMSO and the Queen's Printer for Scotland. Figure 121: © Mary Evans Picture Library.